TY

J

PAUL W. HODGE

The Revolution in Astronomy

HOLIDAY HOUSE · NEW YORK

Frontispiece   *National Radio Astronomy Observatory*

The 140-foot radio telescope of the National Radio Astronomy Observatory at Green Bank, West Virginia. Instruments like these all over the world are opening vast new fields of information and theory in man's oldest science.

The cartoon of Surveyor 3 is reprinted by permission from *The Christian Science Monitor;* © 1967 by The Christian Science Publishing Society; all rights reserved.

Text copyright © 1970 by Paul W. Hodge
Illustrations copyright © 1970 by Holiday House, Inc.
All rights reserved
Printed in the United States of America
Library of Congress catalog card number: 70—102430

TO GORDON, ERIK, AND SANDRA

Preface

In the last few years, astronomy has undergone tremendous changes. New kinds of stars, new fields of research, new concepts, new tools, new observatories, and many new astronomers have come on the scene.

This book describes the new facets of astronomy and relates some of the recent history-making developments. It tells about the discovery of the new mysterious radio sources, the launching of the space ships to the moon and planets, and about many other exciting events. These things have caused so much growth and so much change in astronomy that it has truly been like a revolution. Each chapter in this book relates a different step in this revolution, showing how much there is that is fresh and young in the oldest science.

Contents

ONE

New Streets on an Old Map

There's a chance that the pilot of that supersonic jet that just flew overhead may be an astronomer.

Perhaps he is one of the astronomer astronauts now being trained by the National Aeronautics and Space Administration to fly jets in preparation for bigger adventures—for flights to observatories on satellites or on the moon. Perhaps he will be the first astronomer to set up and use a giant telescope in space. He may be the first astronomer to explore further on the moon and investigate the craters that have puzzled astronomers for centuries. Maybe he will pilot a space ship to a nearby planet.

In any case, if he is an astronomer, the pilot of that plane is a far different sort of man from the astronomers of the past, and his life is a far different sort of life.

A year ago he may have been a professor of astronomy at a university. He possibly taught courses with titles like

"The Physical Processes in HII Regions," or "The Interplanetary Medium," and did research when there was time.
With a graduate student or two helping, he may have
worked two or three nights every month at an observatory,
measuring the various properties of stars, galaxies, or gas
clouds. His had probably been a pretty typical astronomer's
life, similar to that of most of the astronomers of the first
half of the twentieth century. But now his switch to a new
life as an astronomer-astronaut is a dramatic symbol of the
revolutionary change in astronomy itself.

The revolution in astronomy began about 1950 and has
been going on furiously ever since. Radio astronomy,
quasars, pulsars, X-ray stars, artificial satellites, moon
probes, exploding galaxies, cosmic neutrinos—all these
things as we now know them would have seemed fantastic,
almost beyond belief, in 1950. It would have been just as
unlikely to think of astronomers flying jet planes, astronomers in space, astronomers shooting off their own research
rockets, and astronomers rising to the top of the atmosphere
in balloons.

While in 1950 a large observatory typically had a staff of
about ten, including secretaries and janitors, now some
observatories employ hundreds. At a large number of col-

Photograph: Mount Wilson and Palomar Observatories

To the ancients without telescopes, a portion of the constellation Andromeda looked like the picture at top. The small
rectangle at the center contained no visible stars. The same
rectangle looked like the lower left picture when photographed
in 1950 by a large, modern optical telescope. In 1965 a giant
radio telescope looked at this same rectangle of sky (*lower
right*) and recorded this pattern of radio emission.

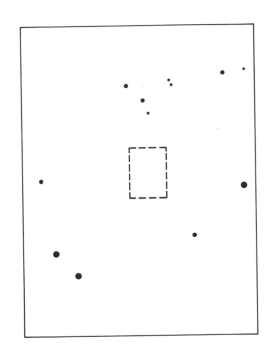

leges, classes in astronomy are as much as ten times as big as they were before 1950. Then an astronomer might drive ten miles out of town to make some measurement with his telescope, but now he is just as likely to fly to Arizona, Puerto Rico, Australia, or maybe Chile to use a telescope. Then he might have used a photographic plate to look at the visible light of a star, while now he might use an artificial satellite to measure the X-rays from that star.

All of this new activity has led to new avenues in our mapping of the universe. The comparative maps that you see here show how knowledge of the sky has grown over the centuries. It is clear that a tremendous amount of new knowledge has come to us in only the last few years. These recent discoveries have revolutionized our concepts.

TWO

Signals from Deep Space

Much of the new astronomy is the result of an accidental discovery made in 1932 when Karl Jansky, a young radio engineer working for Bell Telephone, discovered the Milky Way with a set of earphones.

He had built a huge rotating radio antenna, 100 feet long, to study thunderstorm static. He wanted to know if radio noise from thunderstorms came from certain directions more strongly than others, in order to know how to design better intercontinental radiotelephone systems. After many days of testing he found that there were two kinds of static. The first were bursts of noise from nearby and distant thunderstorms, and he learned enough about these to solve the practical problem he had set for himself. But the second type of noise was a complete mystery. It sounded on the earphones like a steady hiss. Tracing its location, he found that it moved slowly, going all the way around the horizon in a little less than 24 hours.

The fathers of radio astronomy: Karl Jansky, left, and Grote Reber, below. These men, whose faces and names are unknown to most people, broke important new paths in astronomy as surely as Galileo did when he first pointed an optical telescope at the moon.

Left, Bell Telephone Laboratories
Below, National Radio Astronomy Observatory

After many more months of experiment Jansky found that there was no possible source of this hiss on the earth and that it must therefore come from outer space. He also was able to prove that it did not come from the sun, moon, or planets, for they all move with respect to the stars, while the cosmic noise did not. Finally he pinpointed the location of the source in the sky and found that it coincided with the most intense parts of our Milky Way galaxy, the portions that lie in the direction of its center.

Radio astronomy was born. The strongest cosmic radio source had now been discovered. But this new branch of science almost died soon after its birth. Jansky wanted to continue exploring radio sources and even proposed building a large radio telescope, but no one supported his ideas, and he was transferred to other kinds of research. Only three years after it began, radio astronomy stopped.

Backyard Pioneer

A few years later an amateur scientist started it again in his backyard. Grote Reber, a young radio engineer, heard about Jansky's discovery and set out to build a radio telescope like the one Jansky proposed. Behind his home in Wheaton, Illinois, Reber built a radio telescope 31.4 feet in diameter. It looked like a giant dish, parabolic in shape, with the radio receiver held out in front on four legs.

With this movable telescope Reber mapped the radio sky for the first time. He obtained a complete record of the radio-frequency waves coming from the Milky Way, and after several years of working alone he readied the data to publish it. When he did send his paper, containing the first radio maps of the heavens, to the *Astrophysical Journal* for

This historic photograph shows Karl Jansky at the Bell Telephone Laboratories during the 1930s with the rotating antenna that led to the discovery of radio waves from space. The antenna, built of metal rods and a wood frame on four ordinary automobile wheels, is a very humble predecessor of the giant "dishes" of today's developed science of radio astronomy.

publication, it was very nearly rejected. It was so unbelievable and unexpected that the scientist advisors to the journal
told the editor that it should not be published. Otto Struve,
the editor, read it many times, however, and finally decided
to publish it, believing rightly that it was correct and that
it would signal the beginning of a whole new kind of
astronomy.

Today giant radio telescopes like those first built by Grote
Reber exist all over the world. The largest movable parabola
is 300 feet in diameter. The largest parabola altogether,
1,000 feet across, has been carved out of the mountains of
Puerto Rico.

Radio Waves and Telescopes

Radio telescopes take advantage of the fact that the
earth's atmosphere is transparent to radio waves with certain
wavelengths. This radiation is light of very, very long wavelength. Light comes to us in the form of waves that have a
characteristic length something like the separation between
waves on the ocean. But, unlike waves in the ocean, the
waves of light are not ripples of some form of matter such
as water, but instead are a form of energy that has many
of the same characteristics as water waves. Light waves also
have some characteristics of particles, and when they act
like particles they are called photons. In either case, whether
they arc acting like waves or particles, they have a certain
"size," and this is called their wavelength.

Wavelengths for visible light are all very small, but the
same kind of radiation exists over a tremendous range of
wavelength. While the figure for ocean waves may be two
or three feet or more, the wavelengths of visible light are

Grote Reber's original radio telescope, home-built in his back-yard in Wheaton, Illinois.

extremely small, about 20 millionths of an inch. What is called by physicists electromagnetic radiation, which includes visible light, extends all the way from gamma rays, which have wavelengths one-millionth or less the wavelength of light, to radio waves, which have wavelengths up to millions of times longer than those of light.

There is really no fundamental difference between radio waves and light, except for the wavelength. They both travel with the same velocity and they have the same physical characteristics. In the case of radio waves the lengths range from about an inch or so up to miles. The earth's atmosphere is transparent for the range of about an inch or two up to wavelengths as great as about 300 feet. Other wavelengths of radio waves are absorbed in the atmosphere and cannot be picked up for distant astronomical objects.

Because the lengths of radio waves are so great, it is very difficult to resolve clearly whatever is being observed—that is, to distinguish between parts that are close together. Ideally the radio "image" should be like a sharp photograph rather than a fuzzy one, but such big wavelengths create problems and it is impossible to pinpoint the size, shape, or location of the object sending the source. This is because the resolving power of any telescope depends on both the telescope's size and the wavelength observed. If the wavelength is large, the resolution is poor; but it can be improved by making a bigger telescope.

Nevertheless, even with the biggest that we now have, including the 1,000-foot telescope at Arecibo, in Puerto Rico, the resolution is still very much poorer than what we can see with light telescopes such as the 200-inch instrument at Mount Palomar, California. This poor resolution means that

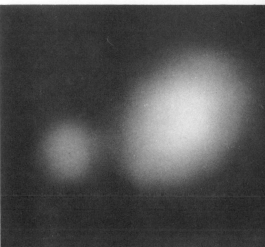

National Radio Astronomy Observatory

The galaxy Messier 51 as seen sharply by optical wavelengths *(left)* and as it might be seen with radio-telescope resolution *(right).*

we see a very vague picture of the sky, with individual objects spread out over a large area. For example, a 60-foot radio telescope working at a wavelength of about 10 inches would see even the very smallest object as a big fuzzy area about the size of the full moon. For this reason single radio telescopes fail when it comes to exact locations, sizes, and shapes, except for large objects.

There are many kinds of radio telescopes and each has its own special use. There are many like Reber's pioneering device; these have large dish-shaped antennas that can be pointed in various directions. His first instrument was mounted so that it could be pointed only along the line connecting the North Pole and the southern horizon; therefore he had to set it and wait for any object he was looking at to pass across his field of view as the earth turned. Now we have very much larger telescopes mounted on sufficiently strong and versatile mountings that they can be pointed in any direction and slowly track the object, staying precisely set on it all during the period that it is above the horizon. We also have arrays of such telescopes in which there are many such dish-shaped objects spread out, usually in the form of an X, or a cross, so that the best possible resolution

The radio telescope at Arecibo, Puerto Rico. The dish of metal mesh, 1,000 feet in diameter, is built into a hole in the ground. The waves are focused by it to the receiver, held overhead on cables.

National Radio Astronomy Observatory

can be obtained. Some of these cross telescopes are more than a mile long and wide.

The newest and most exciting development is the use of two telescopes at very great distances, which can allow a very careful disentanglement of the waves. This greatly improves the resolution. For instance, recently the sizes of some small objects that emit radio waves have been measured using radio telescopes a whole continent apart. It is necessary in order to do intercontinental radio astronomy to have an extremely accurate atomic clock which will precisely determine just when each wave reached each of these

The three-element interferometer of 85-foot radio telescopes at the National Radio Astronomy Observatory in Green Bank, West Virginia. Accuracy of wavelength measurement is improved by using two or more telescopes spaced out in a line.

National Radio Astronomy Observatory

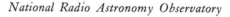

telescopes. The signals are compared, sometimes after one of the scientists carries the atomic clock by hand from one installation to the other—for instance, from Puerto Rico across the United States to California. When this has been done, it is possible to determine very accurately the exact size of quite small objects. This is an exciting and completely unexpected new technical development that is going to be used a great deal in future radio astronomy experiments.

What Makes Them?

There is a wide variety of types of sources of radio waves. At first individual sources were not recognized because early radio telescopes were not sharp enough for astronomers to be sure of just what was producing the radiation. As resolution improved, it turned out that many individual objects were emitting the noise. One of the brightest sources is the sun, though it is not a steady radio source except at rather low noise levels. However, occasionally the sun emits intense bursts of radio noise, and these are especially common during the period when our star shows a maximum amount of stormy activity on its surface.

The planets also broadcast; their radio waves are due to their warm temperatures. For instance, we can detect the radio waves that Venus emits because it has a hot surface, about 600° in absolute temperature units. (Absolute units are like centigrade units, only they start at the coldest possible temperature, $-273°$ centigrade. Star temperatures given throughout this book are absolute.) One of the most exciting periods in the early history of the new research field was the discovery that radio waves from Venus indicated that it has a very hot surface, in spite of the fact that earlier studies by astronomers had shown that its cloud layers were quite cold. This was our first clue that the Venus surface conditions were very different from those of the earth, a fact which has since been amply demonstrated by space probes.

Another stimulating development in radio astronomy occurred when it was found that ordinary neutral hydrogen gas emits radio waves. Hydrogen emits waves in a single line, with a wavelength of 21 centimeters. This hydrogen radiation tells us a great deal about our own galaxy and other galaxies. Radio studies of the 21-centimeter line show us what the spiral arms of our galaxy look like, even though we can't see them with optical telescopes. The discovery of 21-centimeter radiation gave us for the first time a complete picture of our entire galaxy all the way to the other side of its nucleus. None of this distant portion of our galaxy can be seen at all with optical telescopes, because it is all obscured by clouds of dust, which are penetrated by the radio waves.

We also can now detect hot objects in our galaxy, for instance hot gas clouds that are heated up because they are near very luminous stars. Study of their radio output tells us the temperature of these gas clouds and allows us to deduce what is going on in them and how stars are being formed in these areas.

Perhaps the strangest and most unexpected of all radio-noise sources are those that have nothing to do with what astronomers call thermal radiation, the radiation given off by something because it is hot. Certain nonthermal sources were discovered by radio telescopes, and they have proved to be a tremendous surprise in all their characteristics.

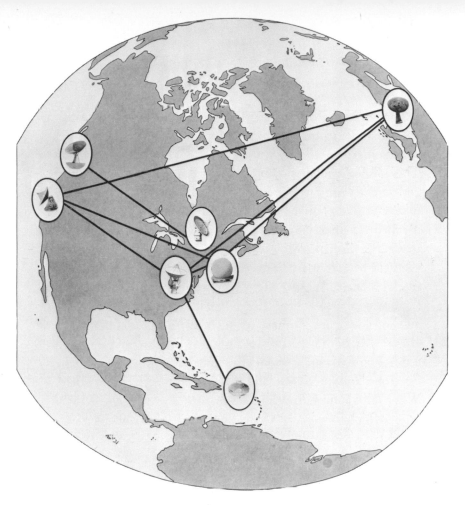

National Radio Astronomy Observatory

Sites of various radio telescopes used in long-baseline interferometric observations. Small objects can be "seen" by radio more sharply when signals received a continent or more apart are compared.

Examples are supernova remnants, which are the chaotic dust and gas clouds that are produced when a star, for some reason, completely explodes and disperses all its material out into space.

The explosion that causes disruption of a star has so much energy and creates so much of a disturbance that we get radiation from the very fast motions of the ejected particles. This kind of radiation is best observed at radio wavelengths, and in fact might not have been discovered optically by now if it hadn't first been turned up by radio telescopes. It is called synchrotron radiation, because a synchrotron, which is a large instrument used by physicists to accelerate tiny particles to extremely high velocities, emits this radiation in the laboratory. We get these synchrotron radio waves (and light waves too) when charged particles, such as electrons and protons, are pushed to such high speeds that they almost reach the velocity of light. It is also necessary, in order for this synchrotron radiation to be emitted, for the electrons and protons to be spinning in a magnetic field. When all of these conditions are met, the particles emit a glow which is equally bright, approximately, at all wavelengths. We see light from these sources at 100 meters wavelength as well as in the ultraviolet and even down in the X-ray region of the spectrum.

Nonthermal or synchrotron radio sources are also found beyond our galaxy. In our own galaxy they are mostly remnants of supernovas, but when we find them at greater distances they turn out to be very much bigger objects, explosive galaxies and quasars. These are apparently caused by gigantic explosions, the nature of which no one in astronomy ever anticipated. They are so surprising and so remarkable in their properties that astronomers are still mystified as to just what has caused them to occur. In the next few chapters some of these exciting newly discovered objects will be described.

THREE

The Mysterious Quasars

In December 1960 a young astronomer took the first photograph of one of the most remarkable and puzzling objects in the universe. The astronomer was Allan Sandage, already famous for his important work in gauging the distances to galaxies. He took the picture with the world's largest optical telescope, high on Mount Palomar in southern California. Dr. Sandage had exposed the photograph for almost an hour, sitting all the time hunched up in the cold observing cage of the giant telescope, perched at the top of the tube, high in the huge dark dome.

The telescope had been set carefully at the position in the sky of a strong radio source known as 3C 48. This source of radio waves had been discovered in England and its position had been determined with very high accuracy by giant twin radio telescopes in Owens Valley, California. It was a strange and unusual source because its size was found

Like this astronomer, Dr. Allan Sandage "rode" the cage of the huge Hale telescope at Mount Palomar to photograph the first radio source that seemed truly to be a star; such sources are now called quasars. The famous 200-inch mirror shows at the bottom of the framework; its parabola focuses a sharp image into the cage.

to be remarkably small for its brightness. Therefore, when Sandage developed the photograph he was not sure what to expect. Would it be a distant peculiar galaxy with chaotic structure?

At just the position given by the radio astronomers there was an object unlike any he had ever seen. It was not a galaxy, not even a distorted galaxy. Instead there was a star, a faint star not unusual in itself, but with a faint wispy

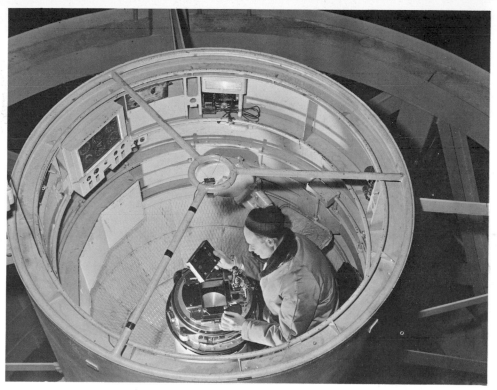

The cage of the 200-inch is seen in close-up here, with the scientist holding a plateholder. As the earth turns, the telescope moves automatically to keep up with it, but minor adjustments must be made by the observer as he checks up through the guiding eyepiece.

line just barely visible to one side of it. The faint smudge of light was pointing to the star, almost saying "Look, this is the thing you have been hunting for."

Never before had a star or starlike object been found to emit radio waves, and never before had a star been seen with a wisp of light pointing to it. "Radio stars" had long before been talked about in the days when radio sources were not identified with anything, but it had since been shown that these sources were never stars. They were always gas clouds or peculiar galaxies. Here seemed to be the first true radio star. Of course it was not a normal star, as the streak of light testified. Therefore 3C 48 was called a "quasi-stellar radio source," a long and cumbersome name that has generally been shortened by scientists to the term "quasar."

Shortly after identifying the object with the source 3C 48, Sandage made a further discovery about it. Using an extremely sensitive light detector called a photoelectric photometer, he found that it had an abnormal color. It was much too bright in blue and ultraviolet light for a normal star.

When Sandage obtained a spectrum of 3C 48, this also proved a big surprise. A spectrum is a photograph of the object with the light spread into all the different colors, in a continuous sequence from the very bluest that the film can record to the very reddest. For a normal star the spectrum is continuous, with light coming from almost all colors. The continuous spectrum of a star has very narrow gaps in it, where little light comes. These spectral lines, as they are called, represent wavelengths of light that did not reach the telescope because they were absorbed in the star's atmosphere. According to their position they indicate the presence of certain elements in the star. The spectrum of 3C 48 was not like the continuous ones at all. There was no radiation smeared out over all the colors; instead there were just a few very bright lines on a nearly black background. These lines represented narrow color bands in which almost all the light from this object was emitted. This type of spectrum, a bright-line spectrum, had been found many times before, but it was always the spectrum of gas clouds, huge masses of glowing gas, and never of a star. Some stars have bright lines, due to the presence of luminous gas in or above their atmospheres, but there was always in addition the continuous spectrum from the star itself. Not only was this the first time that an apparent star was found to have an almost purely bright-line spectrum, but what confounded astronomers even more was the fact that none of the lines were in normal places. Sandage was completely unable to identify any of the lines as due to any known chemical element.

The spectrum of 3C 48 remained a complete mystery until 1963. At that time a major breakthrough occurred. Three astronomers in Australia took the first step by using the immense 210-foot radio telescope at Parkes to measure an accurate position for another radio source, called 3C 273. These astronomers took advantage of the fact that the moon occasionally passes directly over 3C 273, eclipsing it. They were able to determine the exact position of this source by setting the radio telescope on it just before such an eclipse occurred and watching the signal from the source as the moon passed over it. The exact time of the passage of the moon over the source could be determined by watching the signal and noting when the signal abruptly stopped. Early in 1963 this Australian experiment succeeded and it was found that 3C 273 was extremely bright, small and double, and the radio measurement gave a new and extremely accurate position for both parts.

The Lines Identified

Upon the announcement to the world of this position, it was found that 3C 273 coincided with a fairly bright star (bright, of course, only by astronomers' standards, as it was approximately 400 times fainter than the faintest

Mount Wilson and Palomar Observatories

Quasar 3C 273, with its "pointer" wisp of light at the lower right of it. The wisp suggests an explosion, but astronomers are not sure this is the cause. The pebbled effect in the photograph comes from silver grains in the photographic plate, due to great enlargement.

stars visible to the unaided eye). Not only was it a bright star, but it was also found that next to this star was a line pointing to it, as in 3C 48; the second radio source lay right at one end of the jet. It was also found that 3C 273 had unusual colors and a spectrum consisting primarily of bright lines. But the important fact about 3C 273's spectrum was that these bright lines could be identified.

Maarten Schmidt of the California Institute of Technology was the first to discover that the lines were mostly those of hydrogen. They had gone unrecognized because they were not in the correct location for hydrogen lines. Instead they were all uniformly shifted to the red end of the spectrum, away from their normal colors. Dr. Schmidt pointed out that this could be understood very simply but in a rather surprising way. Light waves can be shifted to the red side of their normal position when their source is moving away from the observer. In the case of 3C 273 the amount of the shift is large and it corresponds to an enormous velocity, about 30,000 miles per second.

Astronomers then went back to Sandage's spectrum of the first quasar, 3C 48, and realized that the strange bright lines in the spectrum were primarily the same lines seen in 3C 273, normal hydrogen lines, but shifted even farther toward the red. The shift was so large in 3C 48 that its velocity in traveling away from us was calculated to be nearly 70,000 miles per second.

More Quasars

In subsequent years many more quasars have been discovered. There are now over a hundred of them known. Most are very much fainter than the brightest, 3C 273; and the average brightness of those now known is about 50,000 times fainter than the faintest star visible to the unaided eye. Not all of them are strong radio sources, a fact first discovered by Sandage in 1965, when he was attempting to identify a certain radio source and found in its neighborhood several other quasar-like objects without any known radio source in their positions. But all exhibit the chief peculiar properties originally found for 3C 48.

In 1963 Sandage and a colleague, Thomas Mathews, reported a further peculiarity about 3C 48. They had found, using the sensitive photoelectric photometer of the 200-inch telescope, that when they measured this source on several different nights, its luminosity varied. Over a period of about a year its brightness had changed by nearly 50 per cent. Following the discovery of 3C 273, teams of astronomers at Harvard in the United States and at Pulkovo in the Soviet Union looked at old photographs in the observatory collections, dating back to before the turn of the century, and found that over these 70 years 3C 273 had changed its luminosity irregularly by over 50 per cent.

Subsequently, many other quasars have been found to be variable in brightness, sometimes varying by a measurable amount in only a few minutes. This has remained one of the most puzzling of all features of these objects and makes it extremely difficult to think up a reasonable explanation for them; for if a quasar changes in brightness by a large amount in a short time, then it must be a small object. The size can be no larger than the distance light can travel in that short time, or else the light changes would be smeared out. Quasars can't be larger than about 16 billion miles across. But if they are that small (astronomically speaking), how can they be so bright? How can so much light and radio energy be produced?

As more and more quasars were discovered, more and more were found to have extremely large velocities. At present the quasars with the largest velocities have lines shifted so far to the red that some of the familiar lines astronomers are used to looking at are gone entirely into the invisible infrared. Many of the lines that appear in the spectrum are lines never before seen in astronomy because

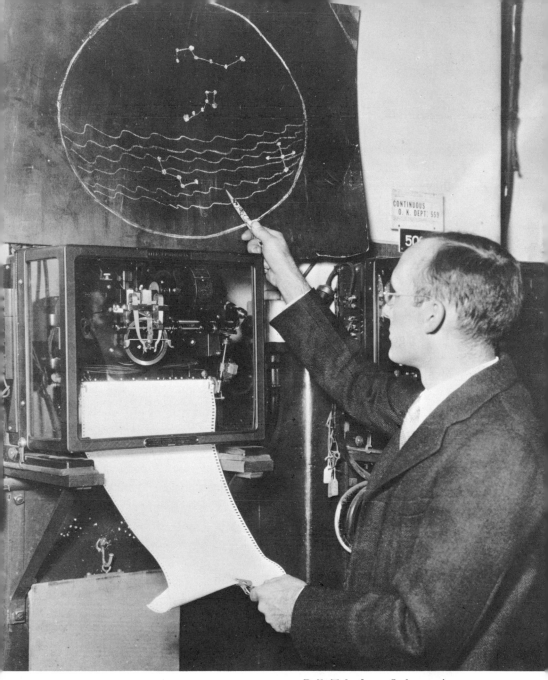

Bell Telephone Laboratories

Karl Jansky at Bell Telephone Laboratories in 1933, pointing to the position in the Milky Way from which radio noises in space were first heard by him.

they normally occur in the invisible ultraviolet. They are, so to speak, appearing onstage from the dressing room.

The fastest of all have velocities that are estimated to be as much as 80 per cent of the velocity of light (this velocity being about 186,000 miles per second). This is so high, in fact, that it is difficult to be sure of it without already knowing the geometry of the whole universe. These velocities are higher than those measured for any other objects and have caused astronomers and physicists to sit back and take a new look at some of their basic ideas.

How Far?

What are quasars and where are they? These are the questions that remained unanswered throughout the history of their discovery and early study. To a large extent these questions still remain unanswered, as there are many puzzles about their nature that are simply not understood at all. But it is now thought that we can at least say where they are.

We know that the farther away a galaxy is, the greater is its apparent velocity away from us. This fact has led, since its formulation about 1920, to the concept of an expanding universe in which all galaxies are moving away from each other at a rapid pace. We feel we can understand why the universe is expanding through the theory that it had an explosive beginning, currently thought to have occurred about ten billion years ago. At that time all of the matter of the universe was gathered together in a small volume, from which it is all rapidly shooting away. Thus those galaxies with the largest velocities are the ones which are now farthest away and those with the smallest velocities are

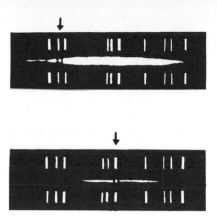

Recorded spectra from the laboratory compared with spectra from galaxies; the comparison reveals the speed with which galaxies are traveling away from us. The position of the two spaces (called spectral lines) at the sides of the white dot *(below arrow)* shows, at top, a speed of 750 miles a second; at bottom, 24,400 miles a second. The displacement of these lines in the light of distant galaxies toward the red end of the spectrum is called the red shift.

the closest. Of course, all the measured velocities are relative and there is no way we can discover, at least for the present, where the center of the universe is—if it actually has a center. Nevertheless, by measuring the velocity of a galaxy we can determine its distance.

The most distant galaxies with measured velocities have speeds like that of 3C 48—about 70,000 miles per second— and their distance is about five billion light years. (A light year is the distance that light travels in one year, at its rate of about 186,000 miles per second.) We think today that the quasars probably also are expanding with the universe, and although they are not normal galaxies (if they are galaxies at all), it is expected that their velocities will give their distance in the same way as for unquestionable galaxies. Therefore the most distant quasars, with velocities of 150,000 miles per second, must be about ten billion light years away.

Are They Really Closer?

The enormous velocities and the very peculiar appearance of quasars, combined with their great brightness in both visible light and radio radiation, make some scientists unsure about saying definitely that their velocities are those of the expanding universe. Because, if it is assumed that these very faraway quasars are at the distances that we calculate on that basis, we find that their total output of light and radio energy is almost unbelievably large—so huge that no very reasonable physical process can be conceived to explain it. Some astronomers have suggested that there may be some other process producing the shift of spectral lines and that the quasars are actually rather nearby, perhaps in our own galaxy or its neighborhood.

The only other known effect that might be similar to the velocity red shift is a movement in the lines caused by general relativity; this is called the general relativistic red shift. This occurs for an object that is extremely massive, so heavy that the mass of the object exerts a gravitational pull on the light. This pulls it down, in a sense, and moves it toward the red. It is hard to think up a reasonable model of a quasar that would have a red shift as great as the shifts so far discovered. In fact, the objects would have to be as massive as a whole galaxy, or more so, and still be only extremely small in size, compared to galaxies.

If instead we say that the quasars are close to our galaxy but are actually moving at the velocities indicated, then we face an embarrassing question: "Why do we see only quasars moving away from us—why don't we see a similar number moving toward us?" The lack of an answer seems to argue against this idea.

What Are They?

Many theories have been put forward to account for the quasars, and every one of them requires a remarkable series of events. For instance, there have been several suggestions that the quasars result from vast numbers of star explosions. We know that stars occasionally blow up, and the event, when it is seen, is called a supernova. Some astronomers have suggested that perhaps a quasar is the result of large numbers of supernova explosions all occurring in a small area. But this seems to mean that an object containing as many stars as make up a galaxy has them all jammed up together and going off at the same time. Such an object would indeed be remarkable and completely unexpected in nature.

Another suggestion is that quasars are small, extremely dense objects in which the number of stars is very large, so that stars collide with each other with faster and faster velocities. This would lead to an extremely hot and explosive mixture of stars and gas and predicts many of the features of quasars, at least for a relatively short time.

Another theory involves the collapse of a massive superstar. It has been argued by astronomers adept at relativity that such a collapse might result in a tremendous release of energy that could look like a quasar.

Antimatter, the opposite of matter, has been the key to several quasar theories. Physicists have shown in the laboratory that all of the particles that make up normal matter have their exact counterparts as antimatter. A particle of antimatter, when it encounters a similar particle of matter, will cause both to be annihilated in an immediate explosion. There has never been any proven discovery of antimatter in nature. Physicists have to produce it in huge nuclear-particle accelerators. But some scientists believe that in distant space there may be stars and galaxies made of antimatter, and that if a galaxy of matter should collide with a galaxy of antimatter, a quasar might result.

There are other theories of quasars, some highly implausible but possibly correct. Some astronomers believe that they may be galaxies in formation, and others have suggested that they may be "ghost" images of more distant objects, images formed by a weird process by which light can be bent, called general relativistic gravitational focusing. It is not known which of these theories is correct, but the most recent discoveries have at least shown that the answer may ultimately lie in the nature of another class of strange objects, the exploding galaxies.

FOUR

How Galaxies Explode

A galaxy that contains one million million stars is obviously a pretty big object. An explosion that completely disrupts such a galaxy and fills it with hot gas and dust is a pretty big bang. Radio astronomy has shown us that many galaxies that we see have recently experienced such huge explosions. One of modern astronomy's big puzzles is why.

About ten million light years away lies a galaxy named M 82. This is of course a vast distance, but for a galaxy is only comparatively small. It is an extremely odd-looking object and we have discovered why it is. About a million years ago a huge explosion occurred in its center. Previous to this it was probably a perfectly normal spiral galaxy, looking something like our own, but not quite so big. From the evidence now seen, we can reconstruct what happened. When the explosion occurred, its nucleus became extremely bright. Huge amounts of gas poured out from this center in all directions, with velocities of several million miles per hour. At the same time vast amounts of dust were thrown from the nucleus, in almost unbelievable billions of tons. As the dust and gas flew out through the spiral arms of the galaxy they collided with dust and gas clouds already there and distorted them, destroying the spiral shape of the whole system. As time went on and the material reached farther out into the galaxy, very little of the original shape was left to be seen, as the dust covered much and the exploded gas shone so brightly that the stars embedded in it were faint by comparison.

A person standing on a planet revolving around one of the stars of M 82 would have had a spectacular display. First, he would have seen an extremely bright spot of light in the direction of the center of his galaxy. If his star were close enough to the center, it may have outshone the brightness of his own sun, so that night may have been as bright as day. Then in a few hundred years the brightness of this central spot would have decreased. If this imaginary person had a very long life expectancy, after a few more hundred years he would have seen a huge cloud of glowing gas gradually grow until it completely covered the sky at night. He would no longer be able to see any but the closest stars. The rest would be hidden behind the luminous gas or obscured by the huge clouds of black dust. If, before the explosion, he had used his telescope to look at our galaxy, the Milky Way, afterward he would no longer be able to see us, or any other galaxy, because of the intervening matter. If that imaginary person is still there in M 82, what he sees now is mostly chaos. He still probably cannot see our galaxy through the curtain of exploded material. It is likely that he can see only nearby stars, and his sky at night still glows with bright, foggy light.

Mount Wilson and Palomar Observatories

The galaxy M82 (NGC 3034) is seen near the top of this photograph; M (for Messier) 81, or NGC 3031, in Ursa Major is seen below, and is a normal galaxy. M82 is a distorted galaxy with its entire face covered with the evidence of a huge explosion that occurred a few million years ago.

A galaxy with an exploding center. This object, called NGC (New General Catalogue) 1068, emits strong radio waves and has a terrific explosion going on right now in its bright center. This outburst will last a few million years.

Mount Wilson and Palomar Observatories

When we look at M 82 now we see a messy, irregular galaxy. We suspect that embedded somewhere in this confusion is a normal spiral galaxy. But most of this normal structure is covered with bright filaments, a bright glow, and vast quantities of dust. We see huge loops of gas jutting out from the center to vast distances. From measurements of its speed, we find that this gas is moving more than a million miles per hour, even though we now date the explosion that produced it at about a million years ago. These filaments of gas extend above the galaxy to distances as great as ten thousand light years.

When we turn our radio telescopes to M 82 we find that it is a radio source. Most of the radiation in these wavelengths comes from the very center of the galaxy; it is produced by high-velocity electrons moving almost at the speed of light in a strong magnetic field. Probably both the magnetic field and the fast electrons were produced in the explosion which disrupted M 82. As we know, this peculiar kind of radiation is called synchrotron radiation, and it is found only in very special places in the universe where extremely violent events have taken place. When large optical telescopes analyze the glow of this system's central parts, they show that much of this light comes from synchroton radiation rather than from the stars in the galaxy. It is this radiation which fills the galaxy and prevents us from seeing its individual stars.

The galaxy M 82 is not the only one that has had such an explosive history. It may be that all galaxies have had explosions like this at some time in their long past. At any one time we can see with our optical telescopes a surprisingly large number of galaxies that have recently had or are now suffering an explosion similar to that which disrupted M 82. There are hundreds of galaxies identified with strong radio sources. Many thousands of radio sources that are probably more distant galaxies have been catalogued. These are not all exactly similar to M 82, as some are much stronger and others are weaker. Some are very much more complicated in their shape and others are simpler.

The Shape of Explosions

In the case of about half of the radio galaxies the radio wavelengths come from a very much bigger area than we can see optically. In fact, the very largest of these galaxies radiates from an area a hundred times wider than the galaxy itself. Others radiate from a small area either at the center or extending over the visible portion of the system.

Of all those radio sources with the radiation coming from a big area, most are double sources. The radio waves shoot from hot spots "above" and "below" the visible galaxy. In these cases the radiation probably results from an explosion in the very distant past, more than several million years ago, and is emitted by electrons and protons that were expelled from the galaxy at a terrific rate when the explosion occurred. They now exist in cones of space at some distance from the main body of the galaxy.

It may be that we see hot spots outside it because the galaxy itself and the material that previously existed between its stars may have prevented these high-speed particles from passing through completely, except in the direction perpendicular to the plane of the galaxy. We can think of a spiral galaxy as being fairly flat, like a plate, and if we consider that an explosive event occurs that throws out material in all directions, that which goes out along the

A galaxy is fairly flat; this one, NGC 2811, seen at a slight angle, illustrates the fact that if electrons and protons were exploded from the center, those that traveled through the thick lateral part of the galaxy would be stopped, while those that traveled perpendicular to its flatness would continue out into space, where they could still be seen millions of years later. Should the nucleus of NGC 2811 ever explode, future astronomers would eventually detect radio waves from the two hot spots shown on this photograph.

direction of the plate will bump into gas and dust that is already there and will eventually slow down. But that which is thrown perpendicular to the plate will not run into much opposition; it will continue going out into far distant space.

A possible explanation of the difference between those objects that show large, double radio sources and those in which the waves come from only the optical galaxy may be that these are different stages in the development of an explosive galaxy. Perhaps the total picture can be explained this way: first an explosion occurs at the very center and we have something that looks like a quasar. It is extremely bright, almost incredibly so, but is very small and does not at first affect the rest of the galaxy. Then the material ejected by the explosion spreads out and causes chaos and disruption in the galaxy itself. We begin to receive radio waves from the galaxy, primarily from the general central areas; then as time goes on, the disruption of the galaxy decreases and the material in the galaxy itself cools down. But the dust and gases thrown out perpendicular to the plane of the galaxy continue to expand outward into space, and we eventually see a very distant radio source on either side of the galaxy. Finally these disperse out into such a large volume of space that they become undetectable and the galaxy itself very slowly and gradually returns to a normal condition.

There is a peculiar type of galaxy, discovered by the astronomer Carl Seyfert in the 1940s, that we now recognize as being closely related to the radio galaxies. They show very bright nuclei with high velocities and very high temperatures in them. It may be that Seyfert galaxies are the earliest stages of explosive galaxies, seen before very much of this exploded material has left the nuclear area.

How Many, How Often?

It is estimated that something on the order of 1 per cent of all galaxies are in the process now of suffering an explosion. This includes radio galaxies and Seyfert galaxies. This particular statistic can be interpreted in one of two ways. Either 1 per cent of our galaxies are accident-prone, in a sense, so that they are at all times suffering from violent explosions, or alternatively, perhaps all galaxies suffer from these explosions about 1 per cent of the time. As increasing information is coming in on the detailed history of galaxies in general, we are beginning to see that the second is probably the correct explanation. It is likely that all galaxies go through periods of violent explosions and that at these times much of the material is disrupted and rearranged. Much of the history of such a galaxy may be erased by this explosion. Calculations indicate that explosions of this kind occur in a galaxy about once every 100 million years.

If our own galaxy had such an explosion in its center in recent times, it might explain the very strong radio source that we observe at that spot. It also could account for the expanding spiral arms that we find near the center and the confused, chaotic structure that radio telescopes detect for the gas on the other side of the center from the sun. There is even a possibility that as the explosions occurred, huge dust clouds passed out through the galaxy and entered into the solar system. If the dust density were high, many of these dust particles would have collided with the earth, falling into the atmosphere and seeding rain clouds. We know very well that if the earth's atmosphere should have added to it a large number of dust particles, the result would be a significant increase in the rainfall throughout the earth. Possibly this would even bring about an ice age.

What Did It?

The total amount of energy released when a galaxy explodes is almost incomprehensible. It is virtually impossible to imagine even how big a galaxy is, let alone how much energy it takes to cause its explosion. Consider an atomic bomb. If we were to take one million of them and place them all in one room, we would have a very explosive room. Now consider taking a very large building consisting of one million rooms and let us fill each of these rooms with one million atomic bombs. Now let us consider building a city, a sort of atomic city, in which we have one million giant buildings in each of which there are one million rooms, each containing one million atomic bombs. Now imagine a country, a very lethal country, containing one million of these explosive cities. Next consider a huge planet and place on this planet one million countries, each of which contains one million cities made up of one million buildings each, with one million atomic bombs in each of the one million rooms of each building. And finally consider a solar system, a star with one million planets, each with a million countries, each with a million cities, each with a million buildings, each with a million rooms, each with a million atomic bombs. And then imagine what would happen if you set off the bombs in this planetary system. You would have the size of explosion that we find when we look at a galaxy in explosion.

What caused the explosions that we see occurring? When they were first discovered it was thought that they might be explained by a collision of two galaxies. We know very well that if two ordinary galaxies should collide, the *stars* in them would not suffer collisions. Stars are too small and the spaces between them too huge. Consider a swarm of bees flying against another swarm of bees. For ordinary swarms, if the two should collide, several bees would bump into each other, unless they were unusually alert. However, to represent typical galaxies, the swarms would have to be very large compared to the sizes of the bees. The insects would have to be approximately 50 miles apart from each other and the total size of the swarm would be about a million miles. Under those circumstances it would be very unlikely for two bees to bump into each other.

Similarly for two galaxies that sail into each other, the stars themselves do not meet. What do collide in such a case are the gas and dust clouds in each galaxy. It is calculated that if such an encounter should occur, these might heat up to very high temperatures. However, this type of hit cannot generate as much energy as is necessary to explain the exploding galaxies, and in no case do any of those we can now see in detail appear to be two galaxies running into each other. In fact, we are not sure that we have seen such a "crash" anywhere.

There are many other possibilities that have been suggested in recent years. Some astrophysicists have thought that perhaps individual stars in a very dense nucleus of a galaxy might explode and set off a chain reaction of star explosions. As we know, stars sometimes explode; their name, supernova, comes from the fact that they appear to be "new" stars, or "novas," that are very much brighter than ordinary stars. If such a chain reaction occurred, it might generate a big enough explosion to form a radio galaxy.

Also, there has been the suggestion that magnetic fields in galaxies gradually wind up as the galaxies rotate, and eventually the magnetic field gets so tightly wound that it discharges, almost like lightning.

Possibly the explosions are caused by the collection of intergalactic matter that the strong gravity of a galaxy sweeps up as the galaxy moves through space. If a large amount of matter is picked up in this way, it may fall into the center of the galaxy, building up a dense core that

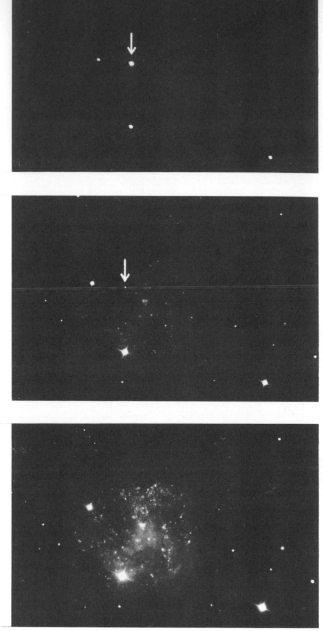

Mount Wilson and Palomar Observatories

The supernova in IC 4182 *(at arrow)* showing how it gradually faded away from its maximum brightness in August 1937 *(top)*. In November 1938 *(middle)* it was much dimmer; by January 1942 *(bottom)* it was too faint to observe. (More stars show in the bottom picture because the plate was purposely exposed longer in this case.)

might explode due to concentration of matter and energy in such a small space.

Many other ideas have been put forward to explain these enigmas in space. They may be closely related to quasars and have a similar explanation, or they may be different entirely. In any case, they have revolutionized our ideas about the "constant heavens" and the quiet and order of the universe.

FIVE

The Giant Flash

Ten billion years ago the universe began. At the beginning it was unbelievably hot and dense. The heat and pressure were so high that it immediately began to expand at extreme speed. The pieces are still flying.

Two very important discoveries made in this century have given us clues about the nature of that great beginning. The first was made in the 1920s when it was found that galaxies were receding from each other, in such a way that the farther away they are the faster they appear to be moving. This led to the idea of the expanding universe, a concept that pictures the entire world of galaxies, whether infinite or finite, getting bigger and bigger as its parts shoot farther and farther apart. Naturally it is interesting, when confronted with this concept, to ask what the universe is expanding from and to try to trace events back to a time when it was much denser and the galaxies much closer together.

In the years since the expansion was discovered, many astronomers and physicists have attempted to look back into the history of the universe. These attempts have led to the concept of an explosive beginning and the coinage of the term "the big bang."

In simplest terms, this cosmology—the science of the universe—pictures everything that exists as beginning in the form of a very dense object. All of the primary material, it is assumed, was "melted" together in a huge sea of elementary particles; only after the detonation did these particles form into atoms and then later into molecules, stars, and planets. Various detailed versions of the big-bang development have been calculated by astronomers and they all agree in general with this type of picture, differing only in the details as to the geometry of all space and matter, the temperature at the beginning, and the division of the early matter into pieces.

An extremely important discovery made in the 1960s has helped greatly to refine our ideas of the beginning phases. Before the discovery there was doubt about whether there was, in fact, a beginning. Many cosmologists believed that the universe might have a limitless history; they felt that the expansion of the universe might be simply an illusion. Another idea suggested that the expansion was in some way compensated for by the production (out of nothing) of new galaxies, to take up the space vacated by the expansion. These steady-state theories, as they were called, lost favor in the 1960s when it was discovered that a faint cool radiation exists throughout space and that this radiation has just the properties that we would expect to be left over from a big bang.

The existence and characteristics of this radiation, which

can be detected with radio telescopes, tell us enough about that big bang so that we now have a fairly clear picture of this crucial beginning period. It also happens, fortunately, that physicists are just beginning to understand the nature of matter—including its behavior under extreme conditions, such as the fantastically high temperatures of that infant universe. Therefore, by combining our new knowledge obtained by using mammoth accelerators and our new knowledge brought to us by mammoth radio telescopes, we can reconstruct a fairly detailed account of the steps in the development of our total world.

From the Beginning

Let us go through the steps from the very beginning to the present. It must be kept in mind that all of these conclusions are based on very recent and still tentative knowledge. Further, they hinge on still uncertain physical properties of matter, and depend on extremely complicated concepts that we must gloss over rather lightly in this book. Even though without many years' study of physics we can't understand the detailed arguments that lead to the conclusions given, we can at least see some of the exciting details of these conclusions and gain a taste for what is going on in the frontiers of both physics and astronomy.

Not very much can be said about why the universe began or what it consisted of before it began. Astronomers can date the beginning by measuring the rate at which the universe is now expanding and slowing down. They find that it started to exist about ten billion years ago.

The first tiny fraction of a second was lost in the fluctuations of time brought on by what physicists call the "quan-

Bell Telephone Laboratories

With this horn radio antenna at Holmdel, New Jersey, Dr. Robert Wilson and Dr. Arno Penzias discovered a faint radiation at radio wavelengths that comes equally from all directions in the universe, and is apparently a remnant radiation from the "big bang." All noise from the earth's atmosphere and the galaxy, as well as from the antenna itself and its receiving equipment, had to be accounted for to be sure the radiation really existed, as something separate.

tum" nature of small things. It is impossible to understand well, without advanced calculus, just what this is, but the result is that if you want to look exactly at "time equals zero," you cannot say anything about what was true then because the question is lost. "Quantum mechanics" smears out the events during this period in such a way that they cannot be reconstructed in any order of time. Fortunately, this mess is only a very brief period that lasts during one tiny quantum of time, which amounts to an extremely small fraction of a second. To put it exactly in seconds, write a decimal point followed by forty-three zeros and then a one. During this brief time we can say nothing whatever about the universe.

The undefinable chaos of this extremely small period at the beginning of the universe was the first of five eras into which we can divide its history. The first era of chaos was the shortest and most obscure. But immediately upon its termination began the second, which has been called the "era of hadrons." This period lasted much longer and it occurred under conditions which we can calculate and understand and describe. The era of hadrons began when time equaled 10^{-44} seconds.

This number is a shorthand way of writing one preceded by 43 zeros and a decimal point, and is a method that is extremely useful in discussing very small and very big things. When we talk of 10^6 we mean one followed by six zeros. When we talk of 10^{-6}, we mean a decimal point followed by six figures, the last of which is one. The first shorthand figure is for one million, and the second is for one millionth. In studying the early stages of the universe, conditions are so fantastic that number words like "million" or "billion" do not exist to describe them, and writing out all those zeros would be tiresome and meaningless. Therefore the shorthand method is used by astronomers.

Fantastic Heat

The density of the universe when the era of hadrons began is calculated to be 10^{94} grams per cubic centimeter. Since water has a density of one gram per cubic centimeter, this means that the universe when the hadron era began was 10^{94} denser than water, an incredible and unimaginably high density. Temperatures can be calculated during the hadron era and they are found at its beginning to have been 10^{33} degrees centigrade. Boiling water has a temperature of 100 degrees centigrade, so you can imagine that fantastic heat existed in the universe when its temperature was 10^{33} degrees.

The era of hadrons is given this name because the universe consisted of a fluid made up of many kinds of what physicists call elementary particles. These particles are tiny things that cannot be split up into other, smaller particles. Physicists have discovered that there are many, many elementary particles of different kinds in nature, and that under very extreme conditions of temperature and density there are perhaps an infinite variety of particles. This is still a very new and poorly understood part of fundamental physics. The hadrons include those particles which physicists find to interact strongly with each other. They include two families of particles, called mesons and baryons.

The mesons include many types of particles that are intermediate in mass between the biggest elementary particle and the smallest. In general, these mesons have names derived from various Greek letters. For instance, the smallest

A cluster of galaxies of various types in the constellation Hercules. All of the millions of galaxies in the universe are expanding away from each other and from what was apparently a central mass of elementary particles called hadrons.

hadron is called a pion, named after the Greek letter pi (π), and it is one of the first mesons to have been discovered by physicists.

Baryons are made up of high-mass objects and include the particles that are the nuclei of common atoms, namely the protons and the neutrons, as well as other high-mass objects included under the term "hyperons." Hyperons are heavier than protons and are the most massive elementary particles. The reason that physicists did not until recently discover hyperons and mesons is that they are unstable particles and last for only an extremely short period of time—in the case of hyperons for only about 10^{-10} seconds. After that brief lifetime they decay into two smaller particles. For example, a "lambda zero" hyperon can decay into a proton, an electron, and a tiny bundle of energy called a neutrino.

These are the hadrons and they are the particles that dominated the primeval fireball during the hadron era, in both number and activity. The other things that existed, namely the photons ("bundles" of light) and leptons (to be discussed below), and possibly the peculiar and hypothetical objects called quarks, were very much in the minority during this period. As the universe expanded during the hadron era, the temperature dropped and the density decreased; as a result, fewer and fewer of the very heaviest particles, the hyperons, could exist. They decayed into ordinary protons and neutrons plus smaller particles, and the hadron era thus proceeded to its end. During this period the photons, which made up the light of the primeval fireball, were fantastically energetic. During the expansion of the fireball the photons lost this energy gradually, and when the average energy fell below a certain critical limit, the photons and neutrons and their anticounterparts began to annihilate each other.

Antimatter, the Mirror Image

We believe that the universe began with an almost but not quite equal amount of matter and antimatter. These two kinds of things are mirror images of each other and they have the property of annihilating each other completely on contact, with the release of vast amounts of energy. For example, physicists have produced antiprotons in their laboratories and they have seen how, when an antiproton collides with a normal proton, both disappear. We believe that most of what we see in the universe is composed of normal matter, such as that which makes up ourselves and the earth, but we suspect that antimatter lurks somewhere in nature at a distant place. Perhaps some of the remote galaxies are antimatter, and it may be that if we should travel to them in some kind of superspaceship we might find ourselves suffering this kind of annihilation.

Whether or not there is now antimatter in nature, we know that it can exist and can be produced. We calculate that throughout the era of hadrons the amounts of matter and antimatter were different by only one part in a billion; they were extremely close to being equal. If they had been exactly equal, all of the hadrons would have been annihilated and the universe now would consist only of radiation, with no matter at all.

The end of the era of hadrons occurred when enough of the protons and neutrons annihilated each other by interactions with antiprotons and antineutrons to leave only a relatively small number of hadrons in the cosmic fluid. The destruction of the least massive of the hadrons, the pions, was the final event. When that occurred, the temperature had fallen to a mere million million (10^{12}) degrees. The density at the end of the era of hadrons was 10^{14} grams per cubic centimeter. When we calculate how long it took for the entire era of hadrons to occur, we find that the time was extremely small; it all occurred in 1/10,000 second.

The next stage in the history of the universe took much longer: an entire ten seconds. This is called the "lepton era," because most of the particles during this period are what physicists call leptons. The leptons are electrons, both the usual negative and the positive ones (positrons), muons (tiny unstable particles first thought to be related to the mesons), and neutrinos and antineutrinos (bundles of energy so small that they have no mass and no weight when at rest). There were very few heavy particles left and the only other significant constituents of the universe were the still highly energetic photons.

The most important event during this period of the universe concerned the neutrinos. Neutrinos are so small that they do not react with other objects readily. In fact, they pass through just about everything, including you, the earth, and the sun. During the lepton era, neutrinos existed in a larger and less dense universe than before—so rarefied that they no longer collided with anything. They were therefore scattered all about the universe, completely unconnected with any other part of it. This is called "decoupling," and during this period of ten seconds the decoupling of neutrinos became virtually complete. From that time on, the rest of the universe existed in a sea of neutrinos with virtually no interaction of the two parts.

At the end of ten seconds the temperature had dropped by

a factor of a hundred, to ten billion degrees. The density had fallen to 10,000 grams per cubic centimeter, and the electrons, which had predominated during this era, declined in number to the point where they were about as abundant as the neutrons and protons. The lepton era thus came to an end.

A Flood of Radiation

In the fourth period, radiation got the upper hand over matter. It can be called the era of radiation, because the universe was flooded with photons, and the density of radiation was far greater than the density of matter. This was a much longer period than those coming before and lasted from a point ten seconds after the beginning to about one million years later. During this time the temperature decreased from ten billion degrees to about 3,000 degrees and the density decreased from 10,000 grams per cc. to only 10^{-21}. Protons, neutrons, and electrons were mixed with a dense and extremely bright field of radiation, and although the radiation dominated, it also continuously reacted with the matter. This era ended finally when the density of radiation fell below that of matter. At that time the protons, neutrons, and electrons were combined to form atoms, and matter as we know it began to emerge in its own right. The matter and the light became decoupled so that they did not continuously interact and were not dependent on each other.

Finally we come to the last stage, which we might name the era of matter. This lasted from one million years after the beginning up to the present and beyond. Radiation is densely distributed throughout the universe and what is most conspicuous is the clumps of matter organized into aggregations of stars and galaxies. While hydrogen and helium, the lightest elements, were able to form into their atomic shapes during the radiation era, the other elements with which we are all so familiar and of which we are all made could not form until the era of matter. We now know that these others, the heavier elements, have been formed primarily in stars, both during their normal development and during special explosive events that they occasionally go through.

The mechanisms by which the hydrogen and helium of the universe actually combined to form stars and galaxies are still not well understood. There have been many theories involving detailed calculations of the way large gas spheres condense slowly into rotating objects like galaxies, consisting of stars; and these various theories are probably fairly close to being successful descriptions. It is probably a fact, only recently recognized, that galaxies, and in fact matter in general, owe their existence entirely to a very slight difference in the initial number of baryons and antibaryons at the very beginning. If it were not for the slight difference, the galaxies could not exist and we would not be here to be exploring the universe.

It is also interesting to note that even though we call the era in which we now live the era of matter, it is still very much dominated by radiation. While the average density of matter in the present universe is about 10^{-31} grams per cc., the universe is filled with photons to an average density of 1,000 per cc. For every nuclear particle there are a billion photons and a billion neutrinos. These neutrinos, with a velocity virtually that of light, continuously speed through the universe with absolutely no effect on any matter. The neutrinos produced during the early period, particularly dur-

Brookhaven National Laboratory

This tank, 4,900 feet underground in a South Dakota mine, traps neutrinos from the interior of the sun. The tank contains 100,000 gallons of a chemical called perchloroethylene. Neutrinos entering it affect an isotope to form radioactive argon 37, which is later conveyed to a radiation counter. The deep-earth site shields the experiment from cosmic rays and all other particles except neutrinos. We still have neutrinos produced early in the history of the universe zipping through us.

ing the lepton era, and at that time released from any connection with the rest of the universe, occur at a rate of 10^{13} per square centimeter per second. This means that every square centimeter of surface in the universe—for example, the end of a person's nose—has ten million million neutrinos passing through it every second.

We have outlined a history on the basis of two important discoveries, the expansion of the universe and the cosmic background radiation. If it is correct, then the universe is truly a sea of radiation and neutrinos, and all of the objects studied by astronomers are merely contaminants that have resulted from a ridiculously small imbalance at the very beginning. The fields of elementary-particle physics and of observational cosmology are both advancing rapidly and in uncertain and unpredictable ways. For that reason the historical description given here may not be correct in detail and may, in fact, be altered in only a few months or years. But the general principles are clear and the observations of astronomers are consistently pointing to a universe that had a violent and spectacular beginning as a blinding flash of light in a fluid of strange particles. We can date this beginning at ten billion years ago, and we see that since then the total world has experienced explosion, decoupling, and diffusion into the vast reaches of space.

SIX

The Pulsars

Most of the objects discovered first by radio astronomers have been surprising, but the most unexpected of all are the objects called pulsars. When discovered, they were found to have such remarkable properties that they defied explanation. For two years nobody knew what they were, where they were, or why they did what they did.

After years of planning and construction, finally in mid-1967 a group of radio astronomers in Cambridge, England, had their newest radio telescope in operation. The final tests had been run. All interfering local noise sources had been mapped and studied completely so they would not lead to confusion with real astronomical radio signals. The problem is the same that exists when the music on a car radio cannot be heard as the car drives under a power line. The power line emits radio waves that interfere with what we want to hear. Radio telescopes are so extremely powerful that they can suffer from interference from much less obvious sources than power lines. A distant car or airplane or even an artificial satellite can cause bad noise problems.

By August the new Cambridge radio telescope was in full operation. But the astronomers found one peculiar source that remained unexplained, and that acted unlike other sources. It "beeped" repeatedly with a period of a little over one second, but was present only a small part of the time. Further study showed that its direction in the sky was constant. Whenever it was heard it was always the same height above the southern horizon.

All the usual sources of man-made radio noise were considered, but none seemed capable of explaining the "beeper." Finally it was observed enough times for the astronomers to see that it appeared, not irregularly, but with absolute precision, every 23 hours and 56 minutes. Since this is exactly the period of rotation of the earth with respect to the stars, the source must be among the stars and could not be associated with the earth at all. In fact, it was soon found that it could not even be in the solar system, but must be more distant.

The most remarkable property of this peculiar object was the fact that it consisted of pulses. All other distant astronomical radio sources are steady noise, with only slow changes detectable. This new object instead was quiet most of the time, with brief periods of intense pulses occurring at a regular interval of just over one second. There is a burst of noise lasting about thirty thousandths of a second and then complete quiet for about 1-1/3 seconds and then another burst, and so on.

The period between bursts is extremely regular. Recent measures show it to be 1.3372275 seconds, with no change detected larger than about one part in ten million!

The pulses are not always the same strength. Sometimes

they are as much as ten times as intense as at other times, and no one has yet detected any pattern in the varying pulse strength. Most pulses are themselves made up of sub-pulses, and these are also variable in their strength. Typically, there are three subpulses. This is how they occur: first the strength rises suddenly from below detectable limits, reaching maximum noise level in about six millionths of a second; next there is a decrease in strength and then another rise, occurring 18 millionths of a second after the first; next another dip occurs, followed by a final maximum 30 millionths of a second later; then a decrease to below our detectable limits again, to remain there until the next pulse begins. It is almost like some kind of superhuman music—there is a definite beat, there is rhythm, and there are complicated modulations and dynamics.

Shortly after the first discovery, other pulsating sources were found. All had properties similar to the first, and the class of object was given the name pulsar—short for pulsating star, though they were not known for sure to be stars. The newly discovered pulsars have periods as short as 0.033094530 seconds and as long as 1.57905 seconds. They have been named according to their location in the sky. The first discovered is called CP 1919, where CP stands for Cambridge Pulsating source and 1919 is an abbreviation for its celestial coordinates.

The Location Mystery

Where are the pulsars? For all but one, we know only their directions, as given by their positions in the sky. Their distances are much harder to figure out. The first clue about distances suggested that the pulsars were in our own Milky Way galaxy, not very far from the sun, as stars

The Milky Way, a panoramic view made up of five separate photographs. This is our own galaxy, as seen through the dense part of it from the area of our own star, the sun. Black masses are dust clouds. Pulsars are apparently located within the Milky Way, relatively near the sun.

Mount Wilson and Palomar Observatories

go. The clue came from a peculiar effect noticed by the Cambridge radio astronomers shortly after the first discovery. They found that the pulses occurred at different frequencies at different times. They were heard first at high, then later at lower and lower frequencies. If they could be picked up on an ordinary radio, for instance, we would hear them first at one end of the dial and then they would sweep across it to the other end in about two seconds.

This peculiar effect could be explained by the fact that interstellar space is not a perfect vacuum. It contains a very few tiny particles, mostly electrons, protons, and hydrogen atoms. The presence of the free electrons, with their electric charge, causes interstellar space to act like a weak plasma. A plasma is a cloud of charged particles, and plasmas have interesting effects on radio waves that pass through them. For one thing, the "index of refraction," the quantity that tells how much the waves are slowed down by the material, is not constant in a plasma, but is different for various wavelengths. Therefore, since the speed of the radio waves depends on the index of refraction, the waves from a pulsar travel to us with different speeds, according to the different frequencies present in the wave. Thus we hear the pulse first at the frequency that the plasma allows to travel the fastest; the other frequencies are heard later.

The Cambridge astronomers quickly realized that this fact might give a measure of the distance to a pulsar. They assumed that all delay is due to the interstellar plasma and that the number of electrons in interstellar space is about one or two per ten cubic inches. Then the path length of the wave through space is given by the delay of the lower frequencies. For CP 1919, the distance would turn out to be about 200 light years. The hitch was that both assumptions could be wrong. The delay might be partly or completely caused by a strong plasma right at the pulsar, or their estimate of the electron density in intersteller space might be a poor guess. In either case, the distance measured this way would be wrong. Some recent measurements of the amount of gas in the directions of several pulsars indicated that there are actually far too few electrons to produce the observed effect, and the distances to pulsars remained still a complete mystery.

Although pulsars have been "heard" at radio wavelengths since 1967, nobody saw one until almost two years later. As soon as the radio astronomers had measured an accurate position for CP 1919 in the sky, almost everybody tried to find a star at that spot. There were two stars, both extremely faint, at the specified point. The brighter one was luminous enough to study and it was found to be a perfectly ordinary, normal star with nothing to suggest any connection with the pulsar. Its light did not pulsate. The other star, too faint to study much, also appeared to be basically normal.

An exciting new development occurred in October 1968 when astronomers used the giant 300-foot radio telescope of the United States National Observatory to look for pulsars. One new discovery, called NP 0532, was found to be in the direction of the Crab Nebula, the gaseous remnant of a supernova, a giant explosive star that flared out in 1054 A.D., at which time it was observed by Chinese astronomers. The Crab Nebula is a remarkable object, emitting X rays, cosmic rays, gamma rays, ultraviolet, visible, infrared, and radio radiation. Thus it was an exciting discovery to find that it also might contain a pulsar.

On January 15, 1969, three young Arizona astronomers, Bill Cocke, Michael Disney, and Don Taylor, saw this pulsar

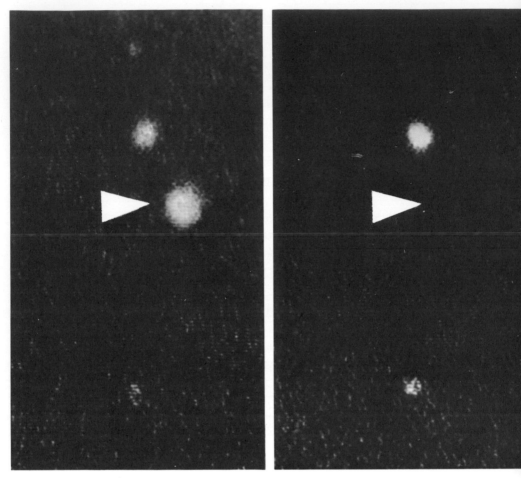

Lick Observatory

This pulsar, NP 0532, in the Crab Nebula, "turns itself on"—
and off—at regular intervals. Picture at left shows pulsar
(at pointer); at right it has disappeared. Since it flashes 33
times a second, a special technique was used to record it: a
disk with a hole in it scanned the star's image, spinning slightly
more slowly than the flash rate of the pulsar. Light from the
pulses was stored electronically to build an image on film.

for the first time. Centering their 36-inch telescope on one of two close faint stars near the center of the Crab, they electronically analyzed the light and discovered that it pulsed with exactly the same period as NP 0532. Although visually it did not blink, their instruments showed that its light is actually made up of short bursts of light, appearing every 3/100 of a second, with darkness in between.

Not only is NP 0532 one of the pulsars with the shortest periods, but it also must be very young, namely a little less than 1,000 years old. Furthermore, NP 0532 has a slowly increasing period. Records from previously unrecognized X-ray observations of pulses in 1967 allowed Rice University scientists to calculate that the slowdown rate is 36.51 millionths of a second per day.

How Big?

The size of a pulsar can be estimated from the pulse duration. If a pulsar emits radiation in all directions, then it must be smaller than the distance that radio waves could go in the time that we detect a distinct pulse. Otherwise the pulse would be smeared out over a longer time interval. This is a similar argument to that used for quasar sizes in Chapter 3. The emitting regions are calculated to be only 500 miles or less across, if we consider the subpulses' duration. This is a remarkable result—how can something so small send so much energy over such a large distance?

So far, theories to explain pulsars center around these questions: First, how can the period be so regular? Is it due to rapid rotation of a source or to pulsation? Second, how can the period be so short? Normal stars that rotate take days or, at the very least, hours to rotate, not seconds; and stars that pulsate have periods ranging from hours up to years. Third, how can it be so small? The only known objects small enough to be pulsars are collapsed stars and planets. Fourth, why is at least one of them (NP 0532) associated with a supernova remnant?

Superhuman Races?

The first theory that tempted the mind was that the pulses are artificial signals being sent out by a superhuman race of space travelers. Their regularity and seemingly coded modulations suggest hyperpowerful radio beacons carrying navigational information for interstellar space ships.

There were two arguments that were used against this theory. First, if the radio beacon sends out these bursts in all directions, then the total power needed is unbelievably large—about 10^{20} watts, more than a million billion times the power of a normal radio station. In order to generate that much power the space station would have to burn up whole planets for fuel. If they don't emit radio waves in all directions, but use a huge parabaloid antenna like that of a radio telescope to point the signal in only one direction, then the necessary power can be much less. If it is assumed that some reasonable though still superhuman power is available to the space station, then we find that all of the pulsars we are aware of are pointing very narrowly right at us. Why? If it just happens that these point at us, and there are others pointing randomly in all directions, then we calculate that the total number of them in our galaxy must be fantastic— the galaxy would have to be teeming with superhumans. It would seem remarkable that none has come and properly introduced himself.

The Crab Nebula in the constellation Taurus, the gas left over from a supernova explosion of centuries ago. The pulsar NP 0532 is found in this location.

Another argument facing the space-beacon theory was that pulsars do not seem obviously to be useful as navigational aids. We use radio beacons for air and sea navigation because light cannot penetrate clouds and fog and because radio waves are bounced along between surface and upper atmosphere over large distances on the earth. In outer space there are few clouds, no fog, and no surface or atmosphere, and therefore no obvious need for radio beacons. The stars themselves are easier to use for navigation than pulsars would be. Not only do navigators at sea use the stars when they can, but space probes that we have sent to the moon, Mars, and Venus also use the ordinary light of stars for their most accurate navigation.

If pulsars are not the brain children of some superrace, what are they? Can nature come up with something that bizarre? There are two kinds of stars that are small enough and faint enough to be pulsars. These are the dregs of the galaxy, the final stages of stellar evolution, when stars can no longer make energy enough to shine and they collapse. White dwarfs are small, about the size of the earth, and very faint, so faint that we have detected only a few dozen. Could some unexplained natural explosion occurring in the thin atmosphere of a white dwarf cause it to pulsate with a short period, with nuclear energy thereby generated in its atmosphere? This would be something like taking the earth, giving it a punch, watching it vibrate, and seeing that with every vibration the atmosphere goes off like a super-sized hydrogen bomb. It is the "bomb" that generates the pulses in this theory. The strongest argument against this idea is the fact that when a careful calculation is made of how short a period a pulsating white dwarf can have, it turns out to be five seconds, nothing shorter. In fact, in order to have enough atmosphere to generate the pulses properly, it has to have a period of at least 50 seconds.

Another idea suggested that pulsars are white dwarfs that are rapidly rotating. On one side there is an explosive region

Observation of pulsars, quasars, and other radio-wave objects improves through the years as larger and more delicately adjusted radio telescopes are constructed. This impressive "dish," among the largest in the world, is at Stanford University in California.

that is emitting intense radio waves, which we receive only when that side of the star is pointing toward us. But this theory meets trouble: it is hard to conceive that a reasonable white dwarf can rotate fast enough. A star the size of the earth rotating with a period of 3/100 second, like the period of NP 0532, would have a velocity at its surface of 800,000 miles per second, more than the velocity of light!

Another kind of collapsed star, one that has been involved more successfully in pulsar theories, is the neutron star. Until 1969 no one had ever seen a neutron star; they had been so far entirely theoretical. They consist of collapsed stars that are made up entirely of neutrons—no chemical elements whatever exist, as they are all broken down by the tremendous pressures in the star. Neutrons, which are fundamental, basic particles, are the main things that can exist under the conditions calculated for these objects. Neutron stars are very much denser than white dwarfs. In fact, they are so dense that, if pulsars are *pulsating* neutron stars, their periods are too long rather than too short. The longest pulsation period for a neutron star is calculated to be only about 1/1000 second.

A *rotating* neutron star is a somewhat more promising possibility. Such an object would be the right size and would have the right period. Furthermore, it would gradually slow down, as observed at least for NP 0532, and it is the type of object that might be the remains of a massive supernova explosion. The pulses may be the result of an active, highly energetic spot on the star, which is bound up in a strong magnetic field. As the star rotates, this active area points at us, and the field channels the radiation toward us as from a cannon. This possible explanation has not yet been worked out in great detail but so far it looks very good.

There is no proven explanation of the pulsars and yet they have already opened a whole new field of work. New techniques, new theories, and new instruments are being developed to explore them. Where they will lead us is not known, but they have already contributed a large part to the revolution in astronomy.

SEVEN

The Noisy Planet

Many times great progress in astronomy has occurred because of accidental discoveries. The uncovering of radio waves from outer space, of the exploding galaxies, the pulsars, and the quasars were due to chance. Another of these surprises occurred in 1955 when two young astronomers, K. L. Franklin and Bernard Burke, stumbled upon a "broadcast" that has led to a whole new field of radio astronomy.

This occurred in a farmyard in the countryside not far from Washington, D.C. There in open fields the Carnegie Institution had put together a large and remarkable new radio telescope. Early in 1955 Franklin and Burke were testing this giant in preparation for an exhaustive study of the positions of radio sources throughout the sky. Now and then they were surprised by the presence of an unexpected interference in the records, a noise that could not be explained very easily. As in the case of the pulsars somewhat later, when this noise was first detected it was thought to be some kind of local disturbance. In fact, in recounting what happened these two astronomers remembered joking that probably the noise was due to a faulty ignition from a nearby car, perhaps driven by a farmhand returning late from a date.

They kept track of the strange interference, however, and soon realized that it happened too often to be discounted as some chance local problem. True, it appeared only in bursts of short duration and in an irregular and unpredictable way, but it did seem to be timed with the stars. It was detected only when a certain portion of the sky was being picked up with the radio telescope each night. The astronomers considered that it might be, in fact, a stellar radio source and they looked carefully at all the star maps, lists of radio sources, and star atlases. But they failed to find anything in that position that could possibly be expected to give forth such huge bursts of noise.

After puzzling over this strange situation and mentioning it to other scientists, Burke and Franklin were amused by one person's suggestion that perhaps it might even be the planet Jupiter. The suggestion was made half as a joke, but just to test it they checked to see where Jupiter was at the time of the observations. Since Jupiter is a planet and therefore slowly moves among the stars, it is not normally plotted on star maps or listed in stellar catalogues. When they noted its position they were amazed to discover that it was in exactly the right part of the sky to agree with the source of this strange noise, and in fact they found that as they looked at their past radio measurements they could even trace the motion of the planet as it progressed. Therefore there was no question but that they had discovered the source of the strange noise. The discovery was amazing to everyone in astronomy, because there was no expectation and no obvious explanation of Jupiter as a radio emitter.

As soon as the new fact was announced to the world, other radio astronomers began to do two things. First, they looked back over their own records to see if they had ever detected Jupiter and not realized it. As it happened, they did find records of Jupiter noise going back as far as five years previous to the discovery of its identity, and from this they were able to put together a more nearly complete picture of just what Jupiter is like as a radio source. The second thing they did was to prepare their radio telescopes properly to observe the object so they might attack the puzzle of just how a fairly ordinary planet like Jupiter can be so extremely noisy in the radio region of the spectrum.

On the Surface

The first thing that became clear was that the waves occurred only at certain times; even when Jupiter was the exact focus of the radio telescopes there were some periods when it was quiet. A great deal of excitement among radio astronomers occurred when an Australian scientist discovered that these periods of greatest activity occurred at a regular interval of about 9 hours and 55 minutes. This was particularly interesting because Jupiter's rotation period on its axis is very nearly the same. The clouds at the center part of the planet's disk show a rotation period of 9 hours, 50 minutes, and 30 seconds; those at the higher latitudes of Jupiter have rotation periods increasing from that value up to about 9 hours and 56 minutes. Therefore it was decided

Mount Wilson and Palomar Observatories

Jupiter, photographed by the 200-inch Hale telescope. The Great Red Spot shows as an oval at left. Above it is cast the shadow of one of its moons, Ganymede, seen at right. Strong radio waves come in bursts from Jupiter, seemingly from a specific part of its surface or atmosphere, and weak ones from several other spots.

that this regularity in the occurrence of Jupiter noise must be due to the fact that the source of this noise is somehow restricted to a certain part of Jupiter's surface and that we hear this noise clearly only when that portion of the surface is pointing toward the earth.

It is now believed that the period of the rotation of the disturbance, now set precisely at 9 hours, 55 minutes, and 29.37 seconds, is the actual rotation period of the solid surface of Jupiter, which we have never seen because of its clouds. Why we should receive radio bursts from Jupiter only when a certain portion of its surface points to us is not clear, even if we set aside for a moment the mystery of what produces the bursts. There have been several suggestions concerning this. Perhaps its ionosphere, the charged upper atmosphere of the planet Jupiter, might focus the radiation toward the earth like a lens. Other mechanisms have been suggested, but none of them seems to be completely adequate.

Subsequent very refined study of the noise from Jupiter has shown that there are probably as many as four local sources on the surface. One of these is very intense; the other three are quite weak and at other locations spread over the surface. There are no clear visible details on the cloud-covered surface of Jupiter that seem to be identifiable with any of these sources.

What Are the Bursts Like?

Sometimes the bursts of waves last only a few seconds and in other cases they go on for many hours. At any given occasion many eruptions are usually recorded during the period when the appropriate part of Jupiter is pointing toward the earth. Some of these are long and some are short in duration but they come fairly quickly one after another. Each is very complex, consisting of many short pulses. Some of these last only a very small fraction of a second, and there has been some argument about whether these small pulses are really from Jupiter or whether they are due to disturbances in the earth's ionosphere. Recent comparisons of Jupiter noise as measured from two widely separated radio observatories have shown that the extremely rapid fluctuations in the noise are probably due to the earth's ionosphere but that the main bursts that we observe are truly coming from Jupiter itself.

If you were fortunate enough to be near a radio observatory that is studying the planet and could listen to Jupiter with a loudspeaker or earphones, you would hear a tremendously complex noise sounding like a waterfall or ocean waves, with noticeable changes of pitch and intensity. If you listened to Jupiter at wavelengths in the range of 20 meters, you would hear something like 13 to 20 pulses every minute.

Lightning or Volcanoes?

The explanation of Jupiter's long-wavelength radio bursts is still an open question. There have been many remarkable theories for their occurrence, and most of them have something to do with conditions at the surface of the planet, under the shroud of clouds that we see. For example, some scientists have suggested that lightning discharges occurring during fantastically intense thunderstorms in the atmosphere of Jupiter might be the cause of them. Certainly they would have to be very much bigger and more impressive than even the worst thunderstorms we have on the earth to produce as much radio energy as we receive from Jupiter. This would also imply that certain portions of Jupiter are more prone to thunderstorm activity than others, a fact that may be caused by topographical peculiarities, such as mountains or other irregularities on the surface.

Other possibilities suggested have been that perhaps the

difference in the rotation period of different parts of Jupiter's atmosphere might set up some kind of a mechanism that would convert energy from Jupiter's strong magnetic field through which the gases of the atmosphere are moving. It was thought that there might be large electric fields produced by this sliding of the atmosphere through the magnetic field and that these fields might create huge discharges of electricity which could produce the signals.

Another remarkable theory proposed that the bursts may be a result of vast volcanic explosions on the surface of the planet. Such explosions, whether they are anything like those on the earth or not, would conceivably disturb the charged particles in the ionosphere of Jupiter and cause it to bounce rapidly back and forth. This kind of oscillation might perhaps produce radiation in the wavelengths observed.

Radiation Belts

Jupiter has another peculiarity—huge radiation belts very much like the Van Allen belts that surround the earth. We obtain radio waves from these belts at shorter wavelengths than for the bursts. In fact, we find that these "broadcasts" seem to have the spectrum of synchrotron radiation, like that from distant exploding galaxies. So this radiation apparently results from trapped particles, such as electrons and protons, that are spinning around in the magnetic field of Jupiter at a very high velocity. As these charged particles move, they emit synchrotron radiation that produces the rather steady buzzing sound that can be heard at wavelengths of about 25 centimeters (ten inches).

From the way the belt radiation changes its characteristics

from time to time as Jupiter and the belts rotate, it has been found that the axis of the belts is tilted about 10° to the axis of rotation of the planet. Interestingly, the earth's magnetic pole is also tilted about that amount with respect to the pole of the earth's rotation. Very careful measurements of the size of the source emitting this steady noise indicate that the radiation belts are about three times the size of the planet itself and that they are concentrated mostly close to the planet's equator.

The outermost belt seems to react very strongly to solar activity. About four days after an explosive event on the sun, such as a solar flare, the outer belt increases in its activity. This is just the time it would take most of the high-energy particles thrown out by the sun to traverse the distance between the sun and Jupiter and to collide with its outer belt.

Another interesting fact about the belts is that the outer one is influenced by one of the satellites of Jupiter. When the satellite Io passes through the belts, it cause a disturbance.

There seems to be a better understanding of the short-wavelength radiation from Jupiter than of the long-wavelength bursts, but one clue indicates that the two are in some way connected. This is the fact that the part of the surface which shows the largest peak in burst-type activity coincides exactly in longitude with that of the magnetic pole of the planet, as inferred from the radiation belts. Thus, although we still have no clear idea of exactly what it is that produces the strong eruptions of noise from the planet, we are getting closer to unraveling the mystery.

EIGHT

The Radar Revolution

There was a story some years ago that a military installation in the Arctic was put on the alert when its radar detected an unexpected object coming up above the distant horizon. Fortunately, before any counterattack was launched it was realized that what this radar had discovered was the moon. Our satellite is a very distant object and therefore extremely difficult to reach with radar, yet radar has been made sensitive enough to detect objects that are even farther than the moon.

Radar is an extremely powerful tool because it is possible to get precise values for both the distance and the velocity of distant objects. For astronomy, getting the exact measurement of distance for objects beyond the earth is quite difficult by other means, and radar has brought about a complete revolution in the methods used.

How Does Radar Work?

In principle it is extremely simple. A radar instrument is dish-shaped, very much like a radio telescope. In fact, many radar telescopes can be used also as radio telescopes. The difference between them is that a radar telescope can send out a signal as well as receive it. The dish acts as a giant antenna for sending a signal in a particular direction, since its shape is designed to launch parallel waves. A spotlight with a spherical reflector behind the bulb does much the same thing with light waves. The pulses sent out by the dish bounce against the moon, for instance, and are picked up again by the dish. The size of the moon or other object, and the roughness of its surface, are revealed by the strength of the echo; the time interval between the broadcast of a pulse and its return to earth tells the distance.

The main differences between an astronomical radar antenna like this and the kind that is used by the police to check on traffic are that the astronomical antennas must be very much larger and more carefully directed in a specific direction. Perhaps the most powerful ones used for non-scientific civilian purposes are the radars at airports. These are generally capable of detecting an airliner at a distance of about 100 miles. Such a radar instrument could never detect the moon; it would need approximately 1,000 times more sensitivity.

The next most distant object, after our satellite, and therefore the next easiest object for radar, is Venus, the first planet to be detected by this method. Venus is five million times more difficult to detect than the moon. Mars, some-

Lincoln Laboratory, Massachusetts Institute of Technology

The Millstone Hill radar of the Massachusetts Institute of Technology was a pioneering astronomical radar instrument, which measured the distance from the earth to Venus and probed the moon's surface with detailed measurements. This photograph, made in 1960, shows an earlier form of the radar setup; it has since been changed to operate at a higher frequency, at which undesirable ionospheric effects are lessened.

what more distant and smaller than Venus, is about 100 million times more difficult than the moon. The little planet Mercury, nearest of the planets to the sun, is almost a billion times harder to pick up than the moon. Nevertheless, all of these planets have now been measured by radar, and we know now not only what their distances are but also what their topography is like. For the first time we have some idea of the relative heights of the different parts of the planetary surfaces, and we can distinguish between highlands and lowlands.

How Far?

Perhaps the most important product of the radar revolution is the accurate calibration of the distance scale of the universe. Everything in astronomy ultimately is tied to distances measured in the solar system, the distances between the planets. Up until the time of radar, the only thing that astronomers could do was to try to triangulate on the nearest planets, or sometimes on the orbiting small bodies called asteroids. This meant they had to observe these objects from two observatories separated at different points on the earth and attempt to measure the triangle formed by the two observatories and the planet. If the angles could be measured and if the distances between the observatories could be determined, then a measure of the distance to the planet or asteroid became possible.

The most accurate ticking off of distances within the solar system came from measurements of a few asteroids which came relatively close to the earth but were still millions of miles away. These early calculations determined what astronomers call the "astronomical unit," which is defined

Mars as seen through a red filter. The planet can be detected by radar, though its distance and relatively small size (it is about half the earth's diameter) create difficulties in doing this.

as the average distance between the earth and the sun. Before radar, the astronomical unit was known to only about two-tenths of one per cent, not an extremely high accuracy. But now radar measurements of the distance to Venus allow a whole new attack on the problem. Recently it has been possible to determine the astronomical unit to an accuracy 100 times better than had previously been possible. Now we know the mean distance between the earth and the sun to within just 100 miles or so, an astounding accuracy considering that the entire distance is 93 million miles.

Solving the Puzzle of Venus

The planet Venus has been a mystery for a long time, and only since radar signals have been received from it has some of this mystery begun to be dispelled. It is completely cloud-covered, and no one has ever seen its surface. It was, until radar, completely impossible to determine how fast it rotated on its axis. Some astronomers guessed that it must not turn very fast or we might see some kind of structure in the clouds. Optical evidence suggested that it rotates slowly, and various estimates ranged from four days up to 300 days.

When radar signals were sent to Venus, the picture changed abruptly from vagueness to precision. This is because the wavelength of the signals was changed a little by the parts of the planet that were moving with respect to its center. The motion of the various parts of Venus caused a measureable change in the radar pulse; there was a tiny shift in one direction for the pulse that bounced from the portion of Venus coming toward us as it rotated, and a shift in the opposite direction for the pulse reflected from the receding portion. This minute change could be measured accurately enough to determine the rotation rate exactly.

The radio astronomers found that almost everyone who had tried to determine the rate from optical measurements was completely wrong. In fact, it was found that, unlike almost any other objects among the planets, Venus rotates backward. Most of the objects in the solar system turn in the same direction, which can be imagined as counterclockwise if viewed from somewhere above the north pole of the sun. The earth rotates in this direction, the moon does, Mars, Jupiter, Saturn, and all the other planets do with one exception; radar showed that Venus, for a mysterious reason that astronomers still do not understand, turns in the opposite direction. Its rotation period is 243 earth days.

This behavior has a very strange effect on the length of

its day. Because the planet revolves around the sun with a period that is almost the same—225 earth days—the two periods work against each other in such a way as to make an individual day, as it would be seen by a Venusian, extremely long. The sun rises in the west and sets in the east, just the opposite of what we see on the earth. Because of the way in which the rotation period and the orbit period are similar, the sun moves across its sky only a small percentage of a degree per earth hour. It rises very, very slowly in the west, taking an entire four earth hours just to get above the horizon. Then it inches its way across the sky, moving so slowly that the daylight on Venus remains uninterrupted for more than 58 earth days. From noon until noon on the planet takes 116 of our days.

Radar also shows us something about the nature of the soil on the surface. We have no hope of seeing this with optical telescopes, and without radar our only hope of determining its nature is to send a rocket to the planet to collect material. This method, if it is successfully developed, will provide us with small amounts of information about very limited areas on the surface, but radar can tell us about the entire terrain, though the data are more difficult to interpret. We now know that the surface of Venus is very much smoother than that of the moon. It is, in fact, more like that of the earth. The material that makes up the surface reflects radar waves very much the way ordinary earth rocks do, and rather differently from those of the moon, which has a more porous and crunchy material.

Further interesting measurements of Venus have shown that there are three areas apparently higher than their surroundings, and these seem to be similar to the large land masses that make up the major mountain ranges of the earth. As more and more sensitive radar measurements are carried out, we will get more accurate maps of these features.

How We Were Wrong About Mercury

The planet Mercury has also been a great surprise as far as its radar signals are concerned. It was found from the first measurements that the surface material is very much like that of the moon—rough, porous, and irregular. But the biggest surprise came when the radar measurements told us its turning speed. This had been determined years before from studies of the faint markings that optical telescopes show on the surface of the planet. From these observations it was decided that Mercury keeps one face always pointed toward the sun. The rotation period on its axis was determined to be 88 days, which is exactly the same as its period of revolution around the sun. Therefore half of the planet was said to be always in bright sunlight, with broiling heat, and the other half in perpetual night, with intense cold.

The radar measurements showed that this was all wrong. The actual rotation period is 58 days—far shorter than the period of revolution. After this had been announced, astronomers went back to the old records which had established the longer rotation period and discovered that these actually agreed with the 58-day period as well as the 88-day period. The trouble had come because it is very difficult to determine how fast a planet rotates when you can see it clearly only at certain times. Mercury can be observed optically only when it is fairly close, but not so close that all we can see is the shadow side of it. This means that there are only certain times when the details on the surface can be seen. As it turned out, these were times when, more often than not, a certain side of the planet was pointing toward the sun.

The correct rotation period of about 58 days is nearly two-thirds of the orbit period. Astronomers now think this means that the tidal effects on the planet—the gravitational pull on its crust—caused by the sun might be responsible for its rotation period. The sun is very close to Mercury. When the planet is at its nearest point to the sun in its orbit, the tidal pull on the surface must be very great. One of the possible results of this attraction would be to make the planet's rotation period figure out at exactly two-thirds of its period of revolution around the sun. As soon as this calculation had been published, radar astronomers re-examined their data and found indeed that the very best agreement would be with a period of 58.6 days, which is just two-thirds of the period of revolution.

Mountains on Mars

Mars is also a planet that can be explored by radar. It has a surface that is rougher than that of Venus but not as rough as the moon's. This agrees well with what we know about the Martian atmosphere and the probable smoothing effect of that atmosphere. We suspect that the very thick atmosphere of Venus is responsible for its gentler surface, because with so much air blowing around there is bound to be a great deal of erosion. In the case of the moon, where there is virtually no atmosphere, and of Mercury, where there appears to be none, there is no erosion and therefore the surface remains very rough and irregular. Mars has a very thin atmosphere; there is expected to be some erosion on it, but not as much as on Venus.

The radar measurements for Mars also show that some areas are better reflectors of radar than others, and these data have been interpreted in terms of highlands and lowlands. The most recent studies suggest that the dark areas, normally called maria (Latin for "seas"), are actually higher lands than the surrounding reddish areas. The radar suggests that in fact these dark areas are low mountain ranges surrounded by flat, dry deserts. The early astronomers certainly made a mistake when they called these dark areas seas.

Echoes From the Sun

The sun also can be studied by radar. Pulse echoes from the sun, first obtained in 1959, are very difficult to pick up because the sun itself makes so much noise in the same wavelengths that it largely masks them out. Never-

Across 93 million miles of space, radar pulses can be sent against the sun's corona, or outer envelope of intensely hot gas. Some of the pulses are reflected back to the earth, others bounce away into space.

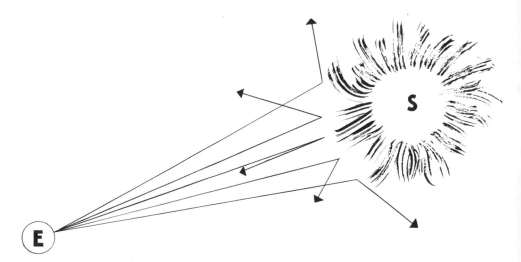

theless, the measurements show that it is possible to use radar to plumb the tenuous outer atmosphere of the sun and to measure the amount of material in this outer atmosphere and its structure.

Sand in the Sky

The first astronomical objects from which radar measurements were detected were neither planets nor the sun. They were the meteors, the small solid objects that collide with the earth as our planet moves in its orbit around the sun. (In those cases in which they have hit the earth's crust and survived, they are called meteorites.) Meteors are almost always destroyed by their passage through the upper atmosphere of the earth and disintegrate into a cloud of dust and vapor at heights of between 20 and 100 miles above the surface. Although radar-meteor astronomy did not really get started until almost 1950, it was more than 20 years earlier that the first radar echoes from meteors were obtained.

A radio signal sent straight up at night is reflected back from the ionosphere, that ionized part of the upper atmosphere that causes radio astronomers so much trouble. Occasionally there are also short bursts of echoes coming from the meteors as they ionize the atmosphere around them in their rapid passage through the air.

Meteor experts now have developed many powerful radar telescopes which have made it possible to detect extremely faint radio meteors, frequent and elusive objects that are as small as grains of sand. Since many of these meteors are too small to be seen by optical telescopes, it is radar that gives us our information on them.

Radar has proved an extremely important new development to astronomy. It has accurately established the entire distance scale of astronomy; it has probed the cloud-covered surface of Venus; it has given us information on the rotation rates of Venus and Mercury, both of which had been wrong; and it is giving us information on Mars, the sun, and small meteors. Someday it will be sensitive enough to study the outer planets. Although we do not at this time see any hope of using radar among stars, we have learned from our many recent surprises that we should not say that anything is impossible.

NINE

Cool Stars and the Infrared

Armed with a five-foot convex aluminum mirror, three physicists at the California Institute of Technology discovered a new type of star. They didn't look through their rather crude telescope, nor did they take pictures with it. Instead, they put at its focus a special device that detects infrared light—light of a wavelength too long for us to see or in this case even to photograph. Their detectors converted infrared light into electrical signals, so that whenever they pointed to a source of such light, they saw a "blip" on their recorder.

These men, Gerry Neugebauer, Dowell Martz, and Robert Leighton, used their infrared telescope to scan the entire sky, not knowing what they might find. They knew that infrared light is emitted by cool objects, such as planets, but is only a very minor part of the radiation given off by things as hot as stars. Nevertheless, they thought it worth

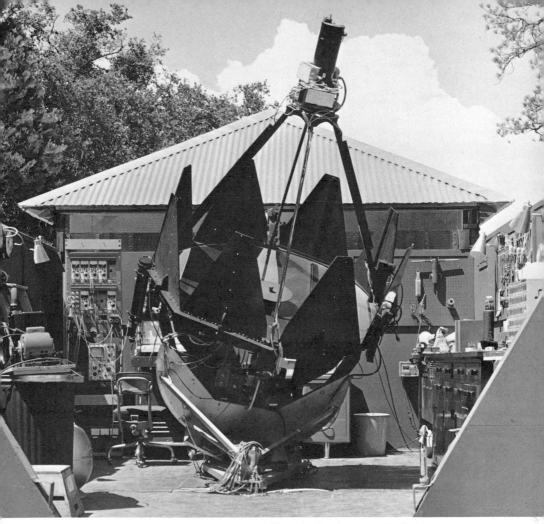

This infrared telescope on Mount Wilson in California has a 62-inch mirror with a brightly reflecting aluminized surface. The infrared sensors, which are kept cold by liquid nitrogen, are mounted on four legs at the mirror's focus. The petal-like flaps cover the mirror when the telescope is not in use. Dr. Robert Leighton and Dr. Gerry Neugebauer designed and built the pioneering instrument with the help of students at the California Institute of Technology, and discovered with it about 20,000 infrared sources.

trying to find among the stars some things that might be bright in the infrared. After only a short period of operation they found such strange objects, which they called "infrared stars."

The nature of these was a mystery at first. But as their positions became better and better known, it was found that some of them could be seen faintly in normal visual light with large telescopes, and these, at least, could be deciphered. There were three principal kinds of objects found to be infrared stars: very cool stars with deep atmospheres, highly reddened stars, and strange objects that are cool but bright and that emit unexpected kinds of radio waves.

Cool Stars

The first category is the least peculiar. They are cool stars, with temperatures of 2,000-3,000° absolute (compared to the sun's 6,000°). Some of them are what astronomers call "carbon stars," because of the large amount of this element and its compounds in their atmospheres. They are well advanced in their evolution and their low temperature is due to their large size and the low rate of burning of their remaining nuclear fuel. Some are "long-period variables," stars that pulsate, slowly enlarging and then contracting, over periods of about a year or so. All have a great many molecules in their atmospheres— for example, water vapor. Only for such cool stars can molecules form and stay together; for hotter stars like the sun, most molecules are torn apart, atom from atom, by the heat. Many of the infrared stars of this sort were discovered to have been already studied and found unusual by their visual-wavelength light.

Hidden Stars

The second category of infrared star is red for another reason. Light of different wavelengths is affected differently when it passes through something. The short wavelengths (blue and ultraviolet) are absorbed and scattered away the most, and the longer wavelengths (red and infrared) the least. This is the reason the sky looks blue to us; sky light is the blue sunlight that has been scattered down to us by the atmosphere, from all directions. And that is one reason why the sun looks red at sunset—its blue light has been absorbed and scattered by the great thickness of atmosphere it must pass through.

In astronomy we find that the material between the stars, the gas and dust, do the same thing to starlight. Light from distant stars is reddened by passage through these substances that lie between us and them. Most stars that we see are reddened by only a very small percentage. But the second type of infrared star is an exception. Some of the sources have now been discovered to be stars so deeply imbedded in distant clouds of dust and gas that only their infrared radiation gets through to be picked up. The visual light that reaches us is as little as one ten-thousandth what the stars sends out, but the infrared is only moderately dimmed.

Maser Stars

The third kind of infrared star is quite strange, almost weird. It is typified by an object in the constellation Cygnus, called NML Cyg, after its discoverers and location. Although it is very bright in the infrared, it cannot be seen at all in ordinary visual light, even with the world's largest

Lick Observatory

Hubble's variable nebula looks something like a diving bird. The area of the head and beak is an object bright in the infrared, known as R. Monocerotis.

telescope. It has a measured temperature of $700°$ absolute, incredibly cool for a star. And very recently it was discovered that NML Cyg is a very strong source of radio waves—but only of emission from the compound OH (called hydroxyl), which is like water but has one too few hydrogen atoms. Astronomers who have measured the OH emission from this object are completely unable to explain it in terms of an ordinary star or gas cloud, because the OH radio waves are so extremely intense. They believe that some kind of exotic mechanism is at work—probably like a maser, where all the energy gets pumped into one particular wavelength.

Infrared astronomy is a new and vigorous branch of the oldest science. When large telescopes are put in orbit, making the infrared easier to observe, it will no doubt bring about even more new and surprising discoveries.

TEN

The Rocket Ultraviolet

The earth's atmosphere, which protects us from bombardment by meteorites, also keeps out other harmful things. It filters out various kinds of high-energy rays such as cosmic rays, that might be deadly to the human race if they got in. Another harmful kind of radiation that is largely absorbed by our atmosphere is ultraviolet light. Mostly we receive light from outside the earth down to only wavelengths as short as deep blue and violet; the shorter part, the ultraviolet, ordinarily comes in from outside sources much weakened.

Anyone who has been in the high mountains on a sunny day knows the effects of only a little extra ultraviolet. At high elevations, with less of the protective atmosphere above, one can get a painful sunburn in a very short time. This is partly because more high-energy ultraviolet rays are falling on the skin, burning it faster than would the normal sunlight at lower altitudes. If somehow the atmosphere were made completely transparent to ultraviolet rays, we might have to use umbrellas on sunny days to protect us from bad burns.

Astronomers, who must grasp at every bit of evidence they can to unravel the puzzles of the skies, are now trying to observe this ultraviolet radiation from the sun and also that from distant stars. They must get their telescopes up above the atmosphere in some way, and methods to do this have become possible only in the last few years.

Above the Earth

The first ultraviolet astronomers used rockets, which spent only a few seconds above the atmosphere before hurtling downward again to earth. The problems were tremendous. Small telescopes and cameras, tough enough to weather the terrific impact of the rocket's return to earth, were built. Delicate mechanisms were developed to point the telescope at the selected star when the rocket breached the atmosphere, and this fine machinery had to withstand the great pressures of the thrust of the launch. Most rockets were launched from New Mexico, and afterwards astronomers had to search the desert for the twisted remains of the rocket, hoping that their equipment was still intact and their film was not ruined.

From these first shots astronomers learned many new facts about the sun and the stars. But the facts were very hard to get, especially because of the very small amount of time that any rocket stayed above the atmosphere. It is for this reason that the investigators turned as soon as they could to satellites. The first orbiting astronomical observa-

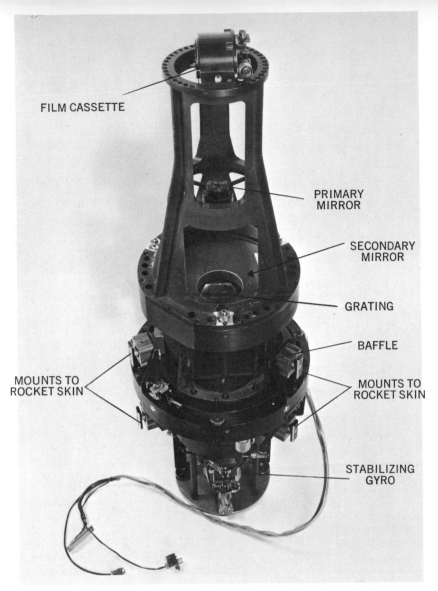

FILM CASSETTE

PRIMARY MIRROR

SECONDARY MIRROR

GRATING

BAFFLE

MOUNTS TO ROCKET SKIN

MOUNTS TO ROCKET SKIN

STABILIZING GYRO

Perkin-Elmer Corporation

This instrument was flown in a rocket by Princeton astrophysicists for obtaining ultraviolet spectra of O and B type stars. To obtain the spectra the camera has a diffraction grating, consisting of extremely fine parallel lines on a shiny surface; a prism would not be adequate because even a quartz prism will not transmit all the ultraviolet. The gyroscope at bottom stabilizes the camera against small movements of the rocket that would otherwise cause blurs in the spectrum image.

tories were outfitted for observing in the ultraviolet, and as more of these vehicles are launched, our knowledge of ultraviolet astronomy increases tremendously.

We have learned most about the sun because it is so bright that simple instruments can be used for it. The solar ultraviolet is very complicated—there are thousands of bright and dark lines in the spectrum, and the brightness depends in an unusual way upon the wavelength of the light and the position of the sun. Perhaps the most important new discovery about the sun from these studies is the information we now have about its outer layers and atmosphere. For example, a careful and highly mathematical study of the solar ultraviolet has shown that part of our star's atmosphere is more than 1,000° absolute cooler than the surface we see. Recent measures say that the lowest temperature in the sun's hot, gaseous atmosphere is 4,600°. Above this, the atmosphere gets hot again, and below it also the temperature rises. The visible surface has a temperature of about 6,000°.

Ultraviolet studies of the stars, though far more difficult, have also given us new insight. Only the very hottest stars, with surface temperatures higher than 10,000°, were detected by rockets. It has already been discovered that some of these hot stars have ultraviolet spectra that tell us they are surrounded by very hot and expanding atmospheres. This is true of the very hottest stars of all, particularly those that are abnormally bright. For example, astronomers at Princeton have used a rocket to study some hot stars in the constellation of Orion. The three stars that make up Orion's belt all have surface temperatures of about 25,000° and they are all "supergiants," stars that are larger and brighter than normal for their temperatures. The Princeton scientists dis-

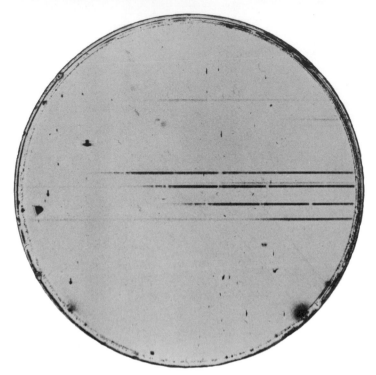

Ultraviolet spectra of stars in the constellation Orion, printed as a negative for clearer detail. The three strongest spectra *(from top down)* are those of Delta, Epsilon, and Zeta Orionis; these are the stars that make the "belt of the Hunter" in the imaginary constellation picture. Zeta shows, from right to left, carbon 4, silicon 4, interstellar hydrogen (the widest in a group of three lines), and carbon 3.

covered that all three stars have outer atmospheres that are expanding outward at the rate of four million miles per hour.

That is one of the big surprises of ultraviolet astronomy, and there are many more. New information on the kinds of substances that exist between the stars has suddenly become available as well, and whole new theories have had to be worked out to explain properly the ultraviolet radiation emitted by even normal stars. At present these new ideas of stellar atmospheres agree well with the observations, but it took the "unexplained" ultraviolet measures to push theoreticians into working hard enough on the problem to come up with adequate models.

This drawing shows NASA's OAO (Orbiting Astronomical Observatory) A2. The cutaway area is occupied by the Celescope, for a systematic survey of the sky in ultraviolet light, as well as investigation of young hot stars, the stars in Orion, novae, quasars, planets, gas clouds, and other emitters or possible emitters of ultraviolet light. The picture shows four telescopes which are coupled to special "uvicon" television tubes, sensitive only to the ultraviolet. Each telescope contains a filter designed to accept different portions of the ultraviolet spectrum. The other end of the OAO contains a separate experiment package. Data obtained are broadcast from the erect antennas; the four outspread solar panels provide electricity.

Smithsonian Astrophysical Observatory

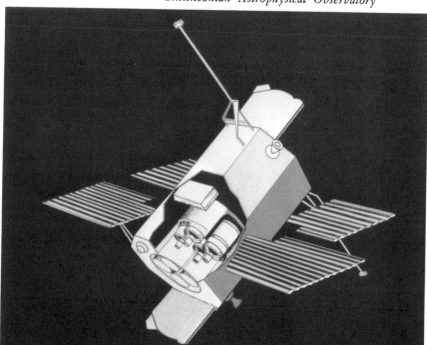

Ultraviolet astronomy has just begun. We've had only a hint of the new breakthroughs that it promises, and as large satellite telescopes begin work we can expect more surprises.

X Rays from Space

X-ray astronomy is another entirely new branch of astronomy that has been made possible by the revolution in astronomical instruments. Since we can now look at celestial objects from rockets and satellites, we have been able to detect any X rays that are obscured by the earth's atmosphere. We now have interesting and surprising data on X rays from the sun, from some well-known exploded stars, from a new class of objects which we call X-ray stars, and from certain distant galaxies.

As we look at shorter and shorter wavelengths on into the invisible part of the electromagnetic spectrum, we pass first through the ultraviolet. When we go to even shorter wavelengths we are in the X-ray region. Normally speaking, X rays have wavelengths between about 400 angstroms and a fraction of an angstrom. (This unit of measurement equals one hundred-millionth of a centimeter.) X rays are absorbed by the earth's atmosphere and therefore cannot be detected from cosmic sources except by rockets, satellites, and for some X-ray wavelengths, balloons.

X Rays on the Earth

Although it is true that cosmic X rays were not discovered until special rockets were sent up in the 1940s, X rays from the sun were detected indirectly many years before that. The earth has a very high layer in its atmosphere that consists of ionized atoms. These are atoms that have had one or more of their electrons torn away from them so that they are left with an electric charge. This layer of ionized gas at the top of the earth's atmosphere is called

This X-ray photograph of the sun, made May 20, 1966, shows the effect of X rays in the wavelength region of 27 to 40 angstroms (with some contamination by wavelengths of 3 to 11 angstroms). Comparison of this photograph with the solar map that follows, which shows sunspots for that date, makes it clear that the spots are principal emitters of X rays.

Photograph by J. H. Underwood and W. S. Muney,
NASA—Goddard Space Flight Center

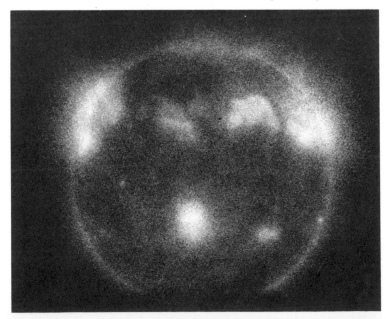

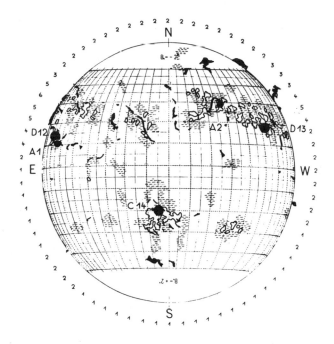

The Fraunhofer Institut map of the sun for May 20, 1966

the ionosphere. For years the way it is produced remained a mystery. The high number of ions cannot be explained by just the visible radiation from the sun itself. There was no way in which normal sunlight hitting these upper layers of our atmosphere could do the necessary ionizing.

Therefore two scientists suggested about 1938 that the sun might be a source of X rays, and they showed that such rays could in fact produce the ionosphere if they were sufficiently intense. This idea occurred to them because at about that time solar astronomers had come to realize that the sun's outer atmosphere, called the corona, is extremely hot, on the order of a million degrees absolute. It was clear that such an extremely hot corona might produce enough X rays right there to create the earth's ionosphere.

Special Films and Captured Rockets

A few years later, when scientists at the United States Naval Research Laboratory found themselves able to carry out some experiments with V-2 rockets captured from Germany after the war, they immediately began looking for solar X rays. Almost as immediately they found them, using very simple equipment. The first successful detection of the rays from outside the earth was on a V-2 rocket flight on which were mounted films coated with special photographic emulsions, wrapped in thin metal foil to keep out normal solar light. When emulsions of this type were developed after being exposed to intense light of all normal wavelengths they were blank, but when they were exposed to X rays they turned out black. When the rocket-mounted emulsions were recovered from the crashed rocket and developed, they were black, and the scientists knew immediatley that the sun does really produce much X radiation.

Subsequent intense study of such radiation, using more rockets, satellites, and occasionally very-high-altitude balloons, have shown that the sun throws off X rays in three different ways. First we find that the corona faintly emits the rays at all times. These come from all parts of the corona about equally.

The second is a slowly varying process that depends on how disturbed the sun is. When there is a disturbance producing a sunspot—a storm area on the surface of the sun—the corona above this commotion also is disturbed and emits more X rays than usual. Centuries of sunspot observation have shown that the spots have an eleven-year cycle during

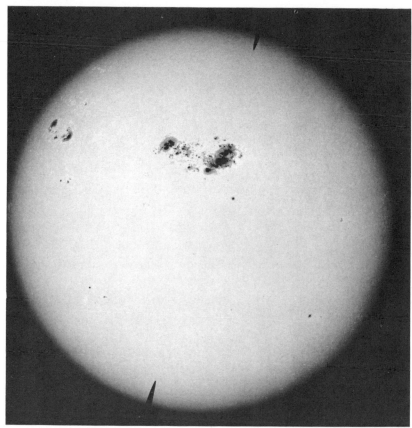

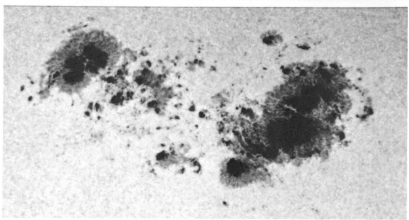

Mount Wilson and Palomar Observatories

The exceptionally large sunspot of April 7, 1947, as shown on the whole disk of the sun and, at bottom, enlarged. The pointers in the upper picture indicate the solar north and south poles.

which they become very abundant and then very rare. The slowly changing X radiation keeps exactly in step with the sunspot cycle, so that we have intense X rays when the sun's face is peppered with sunspots and weak X rays when there are few or no spots.

The third kind of X radiation comes in the form of bursts that occur during extreme solar disturbances. Many of these occur at exactly the same time as solar flares are seen. Flares, which occur on the surface, are produced when a small portion of the surface is suddenly heated to very much higher-than-normal temperatures. Not all of the bursts occur when we can see any solar flare, and we do not

Close-up of a solar flare, photographed by a spectroheliograph in the red light of the hydrogen alpha line—that is, the glow of other gases is blocked out in the instrument and the hot hydrogen alone records the image. One form of solar X radiation comes precisely at the time flares are seen, though it is uncertain that it is a direct result.

Mount Wilson and Palomar Observatories

yet have any really good explanation of the bursts. It is even possible that the two events may be connected with synchrotron radiation such as we discussed in Chapters 3 and 4. It may not be necessary to invoke this strange kind of radiation, but the X rays could conceivably be produced there. Or perhaps the X-ray flares can be explained by the presence of small regions where the temperature in the corona is ten million degrees instead of the usual one million degrees absolute.

X-ray Stars

It was many years after the 1945 discovery of solar X rays that the first celestial X radiation from another cosmic source was discovered. This occurred in 1962, when a group of scientists mounted a series of Geiger counters on a rocket and adjusted them to point in various directions in the sky away from the sun. They detected a source in the constellation of Scorpius, which is generally in line with the center of our galaxy. They also detected another source, but because of the motion of the rocket they were not able at that time to say where this was. So in the following year they sent up another rocket which confirmed the existence of both sources, and pinpointed the second in the constellation of Cygnus, in the summer Milky Way. During this experiment they detected a third point of origin in the constellation of Taurus. This turned out to have the same position in the sky as the Crab Nebula.

In a later flight this same group of scientists discovered that the first source they had seen in Scorpius was really two sources rather close together, one in Scorpius itself and the other in the nearby constellation of Sagittarius. The

Scorpius source is by far the brightest of all in the X-ray region. By now more than 20 X-ray sources have been found and it is expected that many more will be detected in the near future as detectors become more and more sensitive.

Which Objects?

As we have seen, one of the first points of origin discovered was found to lie in the same direction in the sky as the Crab Nebula. From a very precise measurement of its position made possible by observing exactly when it disappeared after the moon passed over it on one occasion, it has been proven that it *is* the Crab Nebula. As we know, this ocean of glowing gas is the remnant of a huge supernova explosion that occurred in A.D. 1054.

Two other X-ray sources have been found which lie approximately in the direction of two other supernova remnants. Therefore we know that at least some X-ray sources are apparently the debris of ancient star blowups, and the X radiation from them may be synchrotron radiation, as is their radio noise.

A very few, perhaps two, of the new X-ray sources lie in the same direction as two radio galaxies, and there is reason to believe that they very well may be associated with these explosive galaxies. But most of the sources are not in the positions of either known supernova remnants or explosive galaxies, and instead seem to lie in the position of faint stars with peculiar properties. Only two of these are definitely identified as the stars producing the X rays. The others are still in some question because of imprecise knowledge of the position that the X-ray experiments give. For many sources we have many stars that could conceivably be the star identified with the X-ray source.

One of the definite identifications is the first X-ray source discovered, in the constellation of Scorpius. Sco X-1, the code name for the X-ray star in Scorpius, was found immediately to be a remarkable object. As soon as X-ray astronomers had narrowed down its position accurately, they telegraphed to optical astronomers in various parts of the world to alert them to look at this position for something unusual. Observers in both California and Japan were among the first to discover a star at just the right place and of just the right brightness. They found that it had a very strange color and quite an odd spectrum. When Allan Sandage, who was using the big telescopes of Mount Wilson and Palomar, first pinpointed this star he was extremely surprised to discover it to be a variable. It erratically changed its brightness as he watched it, a thing that no normal star, even regular variable stars, do.

X-ray astronomers also find that Sco X-1 changes its X-ray intensity, and there have been attempts to see whether the X-ray and the optical brightnesses become large and small together. For instance, some University of California scientists waited at a rocket launching pad on the island of Kauai in the Hawaiian Islands for word about to come from the Cerro Tololo Inter-American Observatory in Chile by way of Tucson, Arizona. When the astronomer using the telescope in Chile saw Sco X-1 suddenly flare up to a bright maximum, he got on a radiophone hookup to Tucson and his message was immediately transmitted by an open telephone line from Tucson to the Hawaiian Islands. Within a few minutes the rocket was launched to observe it. It was found, surprisingly, that the X-ray intensity was lower when the object was bright optically. But when the astronomer at the optical telescope measured the color of the star, from which he could calculate its temperature, he found that it was cooler than before, with a temperature of "only" about 40 million degrees.

A further complication that confounds the mystery of this source is that its motions seem to change in a very short time. These are detected by the shifting of the spectral lines of its light as measured with an optical telescope. The velocity with respect to the earth changes within a few minutes by 60 miles per second, alternating one way and then the next. This is probably due to the fact that Sco X-1 is a double star and the two stars are revolving around each other very rapidly. Sometimes we see one coming toward us and then we see it going away from us as it swings about the other. This idea is supported by the observation that some of the spectral lines, which apparently come from one of the stars, indicate movement away from us at the same time that other lines (presumably coming from the other star) indicate movement toward us. Whether or not the object is a double star is an important question to answer before it is possible really to understand what mysterious mechanism produces the very intense X rays from this and other sources.

What Produces the X Rays?

There have been several suggestions for the mechanisms that might produce an X-ray source. One of the first and most remarkable suggestions is that some, at least, might be neutron stars. A neutron star is a faint but massive object that has collapsed to the point where the atoms that made it up before the collapse have been squeezed together to such a fantastically high density that they are gone; nothing remains in the form of atoms. All that is left is a mass of neutrons packed tightly against each other. Nuclear physics predicts that neutron stars could be formed and that they would be fairly stable. Their central temperatures would be about one billion degrees absolute and their densities so high that although their masses might be about one-half that of the sun, their diameters may be as small as ten miles.

At the outer edge of such a tiny, extremely heavy object would be an atmosphere of electrons. The temperature of this atmosphere would be about ten million degrees, much cooler than the billion degrees at the center. Physicists find that most of the radiation from such a star would be in the X-ray region, so that if we tried to find such a star we would look for an X-ray source. At least one faint X-ray source, the pulsar NP 0532 (Chapter 6), is thought to be most likely a neutron star.

Another possible explanation is similar to that of radio galaxies and supernova remnants: the X rays are produced by synchrotron radiation. At least one, if not more, X-ray sources seem to be identified with well-known supernova remnants that do produce synchrotron radiation at other wavelengths. This is a good indication that the X rays may be given birth by this means.

One of the most interesting theories has been put together to try to explain the brightest X-ray source, Sco X-1, which we can see well optically. Scientists have formed a model mathematically which may explain this strange object. They calculate that if there are two extremely small and very massive stars, like white dwarfs, rotating around each other rapidly (as we suspect may be the case here), we will get X radiation if this double star is embedded in what is called a "plasma."

A plasma is simply a cloud of charged particles. For X rays to be emitted by such a cloud it must be very hot. It should also be what is called a "free-free plasma," one in which the electrons and other charged particles encounter each other but do not interact. An electron flies through the plasma and every now and then has its path altered by coming close to another charged particle, but it is not captured by the other charged particle. (In a free-free plasma an electron can be deflected by either a negative or a positive particle.) The physicists assume that there is a very strong magnetic field in this plasma, and they find that it may be possible for those two little heavy, hot white-dwarf stars, revolving rapidly around each other in the plasma, to produce and pump energy into the plasma, thus keeping it at a very high temperature.

This mathematical model is still quite uncertain but it is an intriguing step toward eventual understanding of the X-ray stars.

TWELVE

The Elusive Gamma Rays

Of all the new branches in the science of our universe, the slowest to develop has probably been gamma-ray astronomy. Years of work and expensive, mammoth equipment have produced few results so far—no new objects, no big surprises, and very few measurements. But gamma-ray astronomers feel that they are at the brink of great successes. In just a few more years, sensitive gamma-ray telescopes in orbit will almost certainly be making frequent important discoveries.

What Are Gamma Rays?

Gamma rays are like X rays, only shorter in wavelength and considerably higher in energy. The wavelengths of the longest gamma rays are ten million times smaller than the wavelengths of light.

The rays are produced in various ways, all involving
high-energy nuclear particles. For example, one source is
the spontaneous decay of a small particle called a pi-
zero meson. This little object can live only about one
ten-thousand million millionth of a second, and then it
decays into a smaller particle plus a gamma ray. Pi-zero
mesons are rare objects and are produced only in such
extremely energetic events as nuclear collisions. We detect
cosmic gamma rays, therefore, only from subjects like
supernovas and solar flares, which are explosive enough to
make the high energies needed.

Although most are absorbed by the earth's atmosphere,
some gamma rays do reach down far enough to be detected
by very-high-altitude balloons. Most balloons used for
science reach up to about 110,000 feet (about 20 miles), but
by using giant balloons full of millions of cubic feet of
helium, scientists can get their gamma-ray telescopes as
high as 140,000 feet, high enough to detect the brightest of
these sources. Almost all of the first observations were made
by such balloons, not by satellites or rockets, because the
complicated and heavy equipment needed to detect cosmic
gamma rays has until recently been too big to get into a
rocket or a reasonable-size satellite. For some wavelengths of
gamma rays, mountain-top observatories can detect signals,
though just barely. One large gamma-ray telescope, for instance, was built by the Smithsonian Astrophysical Observatory on top of Mount Hopkins in southern Arizona.

Most of the first studies of gamma rays from space were
made using a whole conglomeration of complicated physics
instruments, all mounted together in the gondola beneath a
giant balloon. They made up a sort of floating physics lab,
with Čerenkov counters, scintillators, ionization chambers,
and other complex instruments.

Smithsonian Astrophysical Observatory

This 34-foot reflector for gamma-ray astronomy is installed near Tucson, Arizona. It consists of a mosaic of 252 individual mirrors, which here reflect a nearby mountain peak (turn picture upside down). These are arranged in the form of a concave "dish" much like that of a radio telescope. The instrument is used to search for gamma-ray sources in the sky.

Balloons Over Texas

Here's the kind of thing that happens. A group of scientists spend months—perhaps a year—preparing their equipment for detecting gamma rays. They test it carefully, try it out under many different temperatures and in a vacuum, and carefully put it together in a frame that will protect it on landing. When ready, they take it all to the balloon-launch site, often to the one near Palestine, Texas, maintained by the National Center for Atmospheric Research. There more tests are run to check the connections between gondola and balloon, to check the pointing apparatus, and all the telemetering equipment used to radio down the measurements as well as the condition of the instruments and the balloon.

Finally the launch date arrives. Before dawn the balloon-launching crew has the deflated balloon spread out, with the gondola and its load of detectors mounted on a special truck. Everything covers hundreds of feet of runway. As the sky begins to brighten, the helium truck starts pumping the ten million cubic feet or more of helium into the balloon.

As it begins to fill, the top of the big bag rises off the ground. It gradually gets higher and higher until it stands there on the runway with its bottom end still earthbound and its top higher than a ten-story building. The moment approaches for release and the entire crew tenses for this dangerous moment. Depending on winds directly above the balloon, the launch might fail if the bag veers one way or the other before the gondola is completely off the ground The delicate and expensive instruments might be dragged,

Smithsonian Astrophysical Observatory

A 250-foot polyethylene balloon being filled with helium at the National Balloon Launch Facility in Palestine, Texas. Most of the bag lies on the ground uninflated. It will carry aloft a spark-chamber gamma-ray detector.

bumping, along the ground and be ruined. Therefore the truck that holds the gondola must follow the balloon back and forth as it rises, so as to be exactly below it when the cable tightens and the instruments begin their ascent.

If it is summer, the launch occurs at perhaps 5 A.M. The balloon rises slowly, reaching its top altitude at around 8 A.M., at which time radio commands are sent to tell it to begin making measurements. These are radioed back to the ground as they are being made. All during the flight a small aircraft flies along twenty miles below the balloon, trying to keep directly under it to track it and to be prepared for its recovery after cut-down. About seven hours later, at 3 P.M., the command may be given for descent. Usually the gondola is detached from the balloon by an explosion that cuts the cable. Then a parachute is released and the instruments float safely and slowly back to earth, landing perhaps in

This portable receiver monitors and tracks the flight of balloon-borne experiment packages for gamma-ray astronomy. Information, including television images of spark chambers in the package, is telemetered to the trailer while the flight is in progress.

Alabama or Georgia. The airplane often spots it, but if there are clouds or if it is not seen for some other reason, it will be located before dark by the signals its radio transmitter sends out. It may land in a pine forest, and will not be reached by the rented trucks until the next day, but the airplane has probably zeroed in on it and has its position carefully pinpointed. If something goes wrong and contact with it is lost, the plane will search for it for days until it is located, as the instruments used for gamma-ray telescopes are extremely expensive and difficult to put together. As a last resort, there is always a sign on the gondola explaining what it is and telling anyone who happens across it to notify the scientists of its position in exchange for a reward —usually $100 or so.

With the instruments all back in their laboratory and the gamma-ray measurements spread out before them, the scientists then have the job of figuring out what their signals mean and of telling the world about their discoveries. Perhaps they detected gamma rays from the Crab Nebula or from some other unusual object. Or it may be found that they detected nothing, that their gamma ray telescope just looked at a blank area of sky. In any case, the data will represent important new steps on the path to a new branch of astronomy certainly never dreamed of by Copernicus and Galileo.

THIRTEEN

Neutrinos and the Collapse of Stars

Sometimes scientists are forced to guess. Neutrinos were a guess, made by the physicist Wolfgang Pauli in 1930. He sat back and looked at the mess that faced small-particle physics then and gambled on the idea that there might be a tiny particle with little or no mass that could clear up the confusion. Many years later these particles were found and this particular guess was proven correct.

Pauli suggested that neutrinos might exist because he saw no other rational way to explain what physicists call "beta decay." Sometimes a neutron, the neutral particle of the atomic neucleus, decays into a proton (positively charged) and an electron (negatively charged). Since the charge of the proton balances that of the electron, the charge is "conserved"—that is, it is the same before and after the decay. It can be written like this: $n^0 \rightarrow p^+ + e^-$. But the physicists in 1930 also measured the amount that these particles rotated, called the "spin," and this was not conserved. The electron and the proton together have twice as much spin as the neutron. How could this be? It seemed completely unexplainable until Pauli guessed that there might be a third particle also formed by the decay, one that would spin in the opposite direction, restoring the balance. It can be written like this:

not balanced: n(⮑) → p (⮑) + e (⮑)

or

balanced:

n(⮑) → p (⮑) + e (⮑) + neutrino (⮐)

Because the mass and energies of the proton and electron added up pretty well to that of the neutron, Pauli said that the neutrino couldn't have very much mass at all. We now believe that it has zero mass when it is at rest. There is nothing to it except its velocity and its spin, plus (in flight) a tiny amount of mass (m) that it can have due to its energy (E), because of relativity's relationship:

$$E = mc^2, \text{ or } m = \frac{E}{c^2}$$

Since c is the velocity of light, a very big quantity, m is very small, even when the neutrino has lots of energy due to its high velocity.

Because neutrinos amount to hardly anything, they pass right through almost any object without even slowing down. That is why it took years of searching before they were finally detected and proved to exist. On the average, a neutrino would pass through 1,000 light years of solid iron before being stopped.

Neutrinos in Astronomy

The tiny size of neutrinos is the reason that they are important in astronomy. Once a neutrino is formed, it dashes off in some direction, virtually never again coming into contact with anything. The energy that it has is carried off with it, never to be regained by anything else. In this way the energy in the universe is leaking away into a never-never sea of lost neutrinos, and the total usable energy is thus gradually decreasing.

Stars also lose energy by loss of neutrinos. At the centers of stars the temperatures are so high (many millions of degrees) that nuclear reactions like those in the hydrogen bomb continually take place. Some of the reactions are of the type that produce neutrinos, and since stars are all much too small to stop them, the neutrinos escape from the star, never to return. They take away part of the star's total reserves of energy and the result is a shortening of the star's lifetime, and eventual collapse.

Not all of the details of neutrino emission by stars are understood yet; physicists are still trying to figure out more exactly how neutrinos behave and why. Exotic-sounding things like the "URCA process," "neutrino *bremsstrahlung*," and the "pair-annihilation process" are all ways in which neutrinos can be produced under special conditions.

Take, for example, the center of a very hot star, with a temperature of over one billion degrees absolute. Under these conditions the most effective way of producing neutrinos appears to be by the pair-annihilation process. An ordinary

Courtesy of Physics Today

Physicist Wolfgang Pauli at work. Pauli suggested the existence of neutrinos long before they could be confirmed.

negative electron bumping into a positive electron (produced in some nuclear reaction in the star) can lead to a complete annihilation of both. In their place are two neutrinos, which fly off, carrying away the energy of the electron pair. In a large, hot star this process may produce one million million times as much neutrino "luminosity" as the sun produces ordinary light. If the sun actually had such a process going on inside it (it certainly doesn't), we on the earth would be bombarded so intensely by neutrinos that, in spite of their tiny size, we would have an overdose of radiation from neutrinos after being exposed to them a mere 20 hours or so.

Neutrinos are only now beginning to be appreciated for

their role in astronomy. Much new work remains to be done before we understand how important they are, but it is already clear that these elusive particles are involved in speeding up a star's evolution and hastening its final collapse.

FOURTEEN

Particles from Space

Many years ago atomic physicists found that there was a penetrating radiation coming in from space. This cosmic radiation was later discovered to be made up of tiny atomic particles, mostly electrons and protons, and heavier objects such as the nuclei of carbon, iron, and other elements. The particles that make up most of the cosmic rays are moving so fast that they penetrate through almost anything, including this book, you, and even in some cases, the entire earth. In addition to particles, cosmic rays include some gamma rays of very short wavelength.

Cosmic-Ray Footprints

How are the cosmic ray particles found and studied? Many devices have been built for this purpose. Some are as large as a house and others are as small as a matchbox.

The simplest and easiest method is to expose photographic film to them. Because the cosmic rays are largely charged particles, they disturb the atoms in the photographic emulsion as they pass through. The disturbed atoms act just as if they had been exposed to light, so when the film is developed there is a line through it marking the path of each cosmic ray. Very thick emulsions are used, often stacked to a total of several inches, so that a cosmic-ray particle can be followed as far as possible along its path. The width of the track tells how much charge the particle had, and tells what element it was. The spacing of the blobs that make up any individual track tell what its velocity was.

Often a cosmic ray particle will be seen, either in a nuclear emulsion or by one of the other devices used to track them, to collide with an atom in its path. Because of the tremendous amount of energy of the cosmic ray, such a collision usually leads to a breakup (fission) of the nuclei, with fragments flying in all directions. This produces a cosmic ray "star," looking on the photograph like a thin-armed starfish.

Because most of the lower-energy cosmic rays are absorbed in the earth's atmosphere, the observations are made at high altitudes or out in space whenever possible. Tops of mountains—for instance 14,000-foot Mount Evans in the Colorado Rockies—are favored locations for cosmic-ray observatories. Even better data can be obtained from high-altitude balloons, and lately a huge amount of data has come from recoverable satellites.

Even modern jetliners, often traveling above 30,000 feet, are good platforms for observations. This fact was demonstrated by a college student at the University of Washington who carried out a term project of studying cosmic-ray neutrons by asking anyone who planned a jet round trip to take along some nuclear emulsions, especially prepared for this experiment. The result was some fundamental new information on cosmic neutrons.

A Billion Billion Electron Volts

An electron volt is a small unit of energy defined as the energy an electron acquires by passing through one electrical volt. Thus, if an electron is put into a 1,000-volt electrical field, it will get an energy of a thousand electron volts.

Cosmic rays are so energetic that they have energies measured in the billions of electron volts. The most powerful of all have energies as high as a billion billion electron volts. These high energies are one of the biggest puzzles of the rays, because no ordinary process can be thought of that can cause them. For years the source of the cosmic rays was also a complete mystery. Only lately have new developments in other branches of astronomy thrown some light on this puzzle, as we shall see.

Another curious feature of cosmic radiation is that it comes almost equally from all directions. Only the sun seems to be a detectable source (and only of low-energy cosmic rays during solar flares). All high-energy cosmic rays are isotropic—that is, they come in evenly from all directions in the sky, providing no clue as to the location of their source or sources. No matter which way the earth is pointing, no matter where it is in its orbit, the intensity of cosmic rays is the same. We even have fossil evidence that it has been the same for thousands of years, and evidence from meteorites that it is the same at different

Dr. Seth Neddermeyer *(right)* and Dr. Peter Kotzer working with part of one of the many instruments used by physicists to study cosmic rays. This is one end of the streamer chamber at the Cosmic Ray Laboratory of the University of Washington. It isolates muons from other components of cosmic rays.

locations in the solar system. We are bathed in a rain of particles that come at us from everywhere.

High Energy Cheap

Not all people who study cosmic rays are interested in where they come from or why they come. Many cosmic-ray physicists use the rays as fairly cheap high-energy nuclear probes. Where other physicists spend millions of dollars and years of work building giant machines that accelerate nuclear particles to powerful levels, cosmic-ray physicists can just sit back and wait for nature to provide high-energy particles of the sort desired. It is far harder to control an experiment this way, but with patience much of importance can be learned.

As an example of how the rays can be taken advantage of, let me tell a story about a personal experience. When I was in high school just beginning to learn about physics, I got a summer job working in the laboratory of the well-known cosmic-ray physicist Dr. J. J. Lord. At one point my job was to scan with a microscope some nuclear emulsions that had been exposed from a high-altitude balloon and to look for certain kinds of events, such as cosmic-ray stars. One day I was surprised to see a most unusual set of tracks. A fast object, identified by Dr. Lord as a very-high-energy proton, entered the emulsion and then collided with another object, producing a shower of particles, continuing in a narrow cone. This turned out to be a most impressive lesson for me in relativity, for what had happened was that E had turned into mc^2. The entering proton had collided with a proton at rest in the emulsion, and the energy of the collision was so high that some of the energy turned into matter in the form of 22 particles called mesons, which produced the narrow cone of tracks. Such dramatic confirmation of Einstein's formula is fairly common in cosmic-ray physics.

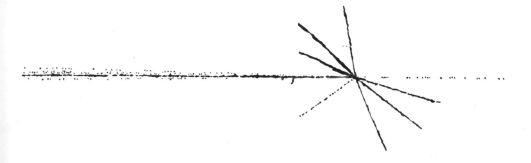

Courtesy of Dr. J. J. Lord, University of Washington

This photograph shows the result of a collision of a cosmic-ray particle, in this case a proton, with the nucleus of an atom in the photographic emulsion. The dots to the right of the "star" were made by the entering cosmic proton; the short arms of the "star" are tracks of the fragments of the nucleus that was hit; and the bundle of faint tracks going off to the left at a slight angle was made by 24 pions that were created out of the proton's energy, according to Einstein's equation, $E = mc^2$.

Particles from the Crab?

We now feel certain that cosmic rays come from various different kinds of sources, although we can't see them actually emitted by any source but the sun. During intense solar flares we detect increases in the low-energy cosmic rays that come roughly from the sun's direction (they are deflected somewhat by the magnetic field in the solar system). We do not "see" any other sources, apparently because they are so much more distant that magnetic fields in our galaxy have deflected the particles and turned them this way and that to the point that they don't reach us from the direction of their source at all.

The most likely sources of cosmic rays are highly explosive events such as we have discussed in other chapters of this book. If our galaxy has ever exploded like a radio galaxy (and we believe it may have, several times), then many cosmic rays would have been produced that would still be around. Supernovas like the Crab Nebula are also good potential sources of cosmic rays, and even ordinary novas produce some. Since the sun, in its flares, is a source, other stars in the galaxy are probably similar sources. Especially good prospects are certain peculiar stars, such as those with intensely hot, expanding atmospheres and those with very high magnetic fields. Also, it has been shown that gas clouds with imbedded magnetic fields can accelerate slow particles up to cosmic-ray speeds. In fact, while it was only a few years ago that there seemed no reasonable source of the cosmic rays, it is now found that there are many possible sources and that all probably contribute to giving us our shower of particles from space.

FIFTEEN

Astronomy in Orbit

With the successful launching of the earth's first
artificial satellite on October 4, 1957, a whole new field of
astronomy began. Space astronomy takes full advantage of
the tremendous feats of engineering that have launched
satellites and space probes, and the number of artificial
astronomical bodies increases at a staggering rate. On October 3, 1957, the earth had one known satellite (the moon),
but only four years later, on October 3, 1961, there were
113 known objects in orbit about the earth. These included
31 instrumented satellites, one capsule, 11 rockets, and 69
miscellaneous metal objects (space garbage). In addition,
four artificial planets orbited the sun. By that date an
additional 32 instrumented satellites had been in orbit but
were by then down, some having carried aloft not only
physical devices but biological objects as well, such as
plants, seed corn, and various animals including mice,

146

monkeys, dogs, cats, and chickens. By now it is almost impossible to determine how many objects are still in orbit, out of the many hundreds of rockets and vehicles that have been launched.

Spacecraft are named according to whatever general series of the same design they belong to, such as the Gemini series, the Apollo series, and so forth. They also have official code names, universally adopted. First comes the year of launching, then a number indicating the specific launching, and last a letter indicating the particular object in orbit, if more than one object is launched by the same vehicle. For instance, satellite 1965 22 A was the Voskhod 2 satellite, from which the first "space walk" was taken. It was the main object launched at the twenty-second launching of 1965. Another example is satellites 1964 65 A, which was the Mariner 4 spacecraft that eventually made a close approach to Mars, transmitted back the first close-up pictures of that planet, and now is in an elliptical orbit around the sun.

There are five chief purposes of an artificial satellite and spacecraft program: political propaganda, communications, surveillance of the earth's surface (for example, for weather data), astronomical observations, and space exploration. The last two are concerned with the exciting new field of space astronomy.

Observations From Satellites

There are three ways in which the earth's atmosphere has limited the extent of astronomical research done by earth-bound observatories. First, the turbulence in the atmosphere has put a practical limit on how small an object can be seen with any terrestrial telescope. A satellite observatory, then, can do a great many hitherto impossible studies of fine detail. Some of the more important problems that can be solved in this way include the study of fine structure on planetary surfaces, especially for Mars and Mercury; studies of solar "granulation" and other fine structure on the disk and limb (the outer edge) of the sun; and measures of precise diameters and shapes for the planets. In addition, we can hope to measure orbits of very close double stars which swing around each other, the fine structure in gas clouds, and the diameters of the expanding envelopes around exploded stars. For the first time we will be able to measure the brightnesses of stars in very crowded regions, such as those in the centers of rich clusters, and we can begin to study the size and nature of the nuclei of galaxies. We may also be able to achieve resolution of very faint stars, especially in other galaxies, where crowding is a serious problem.

Because bad atmospheric turbulence, which causes wiggly images in earth-bound telescopes, originates fairly low in the atmosphere, some of these problems can be and have been attacked by balloon-borne telescopes at heights of approximately 100,000 feet. Other problems require observations completely above the atmosphere and must be carried out from either satellites or space stations on atmosphereless bodies. Because all of these projects require extreme stability of the telescope and because many require very large telescopes, there is a strong argument for working from a very large natural or artificial body. Of the natural bodies esssentially without atmospheres the moon is perhaps most favorable, because of its great size, slow rotation period, and accessibility. One might also plan to use asteroids, the numerous small "minor planets" that zip around the sun, but many of them would be useless because of rotation periods of only a few hours, and large and frequent changes of orbit. But most problems can probably be attacked from man-made space stations that are suitably stabilized in orbit about our planet.

The second way in which the earth's atmosphere limits astronomy is its obscuration of a large part of the spectrum of electromagnetic waves. Only a narrow band of visual wavelengths and radio wavelengths larger than a few millimeters are transmitted by the atmosphere. Most infrared light and almost everything with wavelengths shorter than those of blue light is absorbed by the air blanket and excluded from the earth-based astronomer. Above the atmosphere, instruments can measure waves practically throughout the entire spectrum (except for regions of it absorbed by the interplanetary or interstellar gas). These include gamma radiation, X rays, the ultraviolet, and the infrared. Very little of what we now know about these types of radiation from distant sources could have been learned without the use of rockets and satellites, and much of the future of space astronomy will deal with them.

The third limitation comes from the relative brightness of the night sky. The 200-inch reflector at Mount Palomar, for instance, reaches its limit in about 20 minutes' exposure on a standard photographic plate. It cannot expose longer, because the brightness of the night sky fogs the plate seriously after this time. Extra-atmospheric telescopes will be able to reach fainter sources than can be recorded by terrestrial telescopes, however. On the moon, where there is no atmospheric night-sky light, a telescope of similar size to Mount Palomar's could expose a plate for considerably longer and could photograph much fainter objects. In practice, the exposure will probably be found to be limited somewhat by the fact that the solar-system night sky will be illuminated by a number of sources, among which are light from interplanetary dust (strongest near the sun), the earth's gas tail, the general diffuse starlight from our galaxy, and the background of distant galaxies.

Outside the solar system we expect to gain even more, but it will be years before astronomers can hope to get observing time on telescopes mounted out there somewhere between the stars.

The Orbiting Observatories

The first space observatories are the OAOs and the OSOs. The OAOs are Orbiting Astronomical Observatories, a series of spacecraft that carry various small telescopes into earth orbit, where they radio down their information to satellite ground stations. The Orbiting Solar Observatories, which got a much earlier start than the OAOs, carry special telescopes designed to study only the intense light from the sun. Neither type is manned by astronauts and neither is recovered.

The most exciting results from the early OSOs concerned X rays from the sun. Most of the experiments on the OSOs explore the sun in the short and long wavelengths that are absorbed in the earth's atmosphere and are not visible from here at the surface.

The OAO series of space observatories looks at stars and galaxies in all the wavelengths not detectable from the ground. Gamma rays, X rays, ultraviolet, infrared, and extra-long radio waves are all the subject of one or another experiment on the OAOs.

An OAO, or Orbiting Astronomical Observatory, being checked by technicians at Cape Kennedy, Florida. It carries eleven telescopes designed to investigate the history of the universe. This machine contains 328,000 separate parts and is one of the heaviest and most automated satellites ever sent up. The "wings" convert sunlight to electricity to run the various controls and broadcast data back to earth.

NASA

Astronomy on Other Satellites

Many other satellites, even at the very beginning of the space age, contributed to our knowledge of astronomy. Sometimes the scientific goals were not as important as the more practical ones of testing the safety of outer space as a place to put men. For instance, in checking on the hazards of cosmic dust to space vehicles, satellites measured more accurately than ever before just how many dust particles there are out there and how big they are. Also, in testing for radiation hazards, early satellites discovered the earth's radiation belts. They also mapped out how the shower of charged particles from the sun—the solar wind—bends the earth's magnetic field around behind it, making a tail opposite the sun.

Manned satellites, though chiefly intended to explore and to experiment for future trips by man, also have carried out astronomical experiments. The astronauts in Gemini 5, for instance, took pictures of the *Gegenschein* and the zodiacal light for astronomers at the University of Minnesota. These objects are both extremely faint and difficult to see from the ground, and both are produced by the reflection of sunlight from the small dust particles that lie between the planets.

The most exciting space astronomy, though, is yet to come. Plans are under way to put instruments as large as the Palomar 200-inch telescope into orbit. These giant space telescopes will give us a fantastic view of the universe—far nearer to complete than we have ever had. Astronomers now being trained as scientist-astronauts will probably be among the first to fly up to these huge space observatories, where they will be able to carry out observations that they

Haleakala Observatory, University of Hawaii

The zodiacal light, as photographed by Peter B. Hutchison from a Hawaiian observatory in January 1967. This hard-to-photograph subject has also been captured on film by astronauts in manned spacecraft. The light shows as a long half-ellipse of reflection from dust, primarily meteoritic, and appears brightest in the tropics.

never could have made from the ground. They will stay in orbit with the telescope, living either inside it or in a separate spacecraft tethered to it. They will stay a week or maybe a month and then return with their spacecraft crammed full of new and exciting data. It will often take years for them and their colleagues to process and understand all of the information obtained on just one of these missions.

Clearly, when that day comes, one of the big worries will be that astronomers will be buried under their work, never able to catch up with the fantastic rate of production of space observatories. To prepare for such a time, universities throughout the country and the world are stepping up their efforts to train more astronomers. Young people now contemplating a career in astronomy therefore have an opportunity for success and an exciting life that has never been equaled in the history of this, the oldest science.

SIXTEEN

On the Moon

For centuries men had wondered about our satellite and speculated on what it consists of. Years ago children were told that the moon is made of green cheese. Today even very young children know better. It was proven beyond a doubt in 1967, when a Surveyor spacecraft landed gently on the moon and then chemically analyzed its surface, that the lunar crust consists of rock, though – as we learned later—it is rock with many differences from that of the earth.

The whole world buzzed with excitement during the sixties as each new lunar vehicle completed a new and spectacular mission. The most excited men of all were the astronomers who study the moon, because they saw at last the realization of their dreams of actually sending their measuring instruments, and eventually themselves, to its surface. They foresaw the gradual answering of the centuries-old mysteries about the moon, its craters, its "seas," its history, and its composition.

The Fly-Bys

The first rocket to pass close to the moon (called a lunar "fly-by") was launched in January 1959 by the U.S.S.R. It was called Luna 1, and passed the moon at a distance of only about 4,000 miles before going on to become an artificial planet of the sun. A few months later, in September, the Russian Luna 3 spacecraft swung out past the moon and then back again, taking pictures of the mysterious, uncharted far side of the body. The moon revolves around the earth with one side always pointed away from us, so this was our first glimpse of that hidden part. Luna 3 took its pictures on October 7, 1959, when about 40,000 miles behind the lunar far side, and then it automatically developed the 35-millimeter films and scanned them for radio transmittal back to earth.

Five more fly-bys occurred after Luna 3, including two U.S.A. rockets (Rangers 3 and 5) and three Russian vehicles (Luna 4 and 6 and Zond 3). Only Zond 3, launched in 1965, accomplished its mission successfully, though, as the others were mostly "misses," spacecraft that were supposed to hit the moon but didn't. Zond 3 took more and better pictures of the moon's far side and almost completed our maps of the hidden area. From the earth we can see at one time or another a total of 59 per cent of the lunar surface. Luna 3 increased our coverage to 87 per cent and Zond 3 photographed almost all of the remaining 13 per cent. The tiny fraction that remained was finally seen in complete detail in 1967 by Orbiter 5.

The Hard-Landers

When a spacecraft collides with the moon without first braking down, and is destroyed, it is called a hard-lander. Many hard-landers were intentional, but many others were accidents, when some planned mission failed. Between 1959, when Luna 2, the first hard-lander, crashed into the moon, and 1968 there were a total of 11 spacecraft that had made hard landings on the moon.

The main point of Luna 2 was simply that it was the first man-made object to reach the moon. Ranger 4, the second hard-lander, crashed into the far side of the moon after sending back data on lunar radioactivity. The next object to crash-land was Ranger 6, which sent back important information on the exact mass of the moon, giving us a ten times more accurate value than all methods had given us before.

The most productive hard-landers were the three successful Ranger rockets of 1964 and 1965. They sent back the first really good and detailed close-up photographs of the lunar surface. The Rangers had six cameras that continually took pictures of the moon during the last 15 minutes of the flight. They exposed each picture for a few millionths of a second and then spent 2½ seconds to send each image back to the earth. The three successful Rangers, 7, 8, and 9, sent back a total of over 17,000 pictures of the moon, some of them from so close that objects only a foot or so in size were visible. These were the most detailed pictures ever taken of the moon to that date, surpassing in sharpness the best earth-bound telescopic pictures by a factor of at least a thousand.

The Soft-Landers

The next step, after sending rockets to crash-land on the moon, was to build one that would be able to brake its descent sufficiently to make a soft, nondestructive landing.

The Russians tried first, with Luna 5, which crash-landed, Luna 6, which missed the moon, and Luna 8, which crash-landed. Finally, in February 1966, Luna 9 successfully soft-landed on the lunar surface, coming down with a velocity of about 20 miles per hour, a fast speed, but not too fast to damage the craft. It was equipped with chemical batteries that gave it enough power to operate for three earth days, during which it transmitted back many pictures of the lunar landscape. It landed on the flat plain called Oceanus Procellarum (early astronomers mistook the flat lunar plains for oceans), and sent back details of the nearby countryside —bleak, barren, and rocky.

Four months later the first U.S. attempt, Surveyor 1, successfully soft-landed. It was bigger than Luna 9 (640 pounds compared to 220 pounds) and used solar instead of chemical batteries so that it could go on operating for months. It worked from June 2, 1966, until October 10, 1966, with time out for lunar nights, and after that it was still turned on now and then to check on its condition. During its primary mission it took over 11,000 pictures of the nearby rocky moonscape, and after sunset it took more pictures, some of the solar corona, the stars and the planets.

In December of 1966, the U.S.S.R. launched Luna 13, the third successful soft-lander. It came down not far from Luna 9 and Surveyor 1, and settled in a shallow crater; thus it couldn't see very far. A few months later Surveyor 3 landed in a similar crater, and also had its horizon limited by the rim. Surveyor 2 had crashed six months before, and problems had arisen with Surveyor 3 before it landed so that it was moving a little bit sideways on touchdown. This caused it to bounce twice, coming down 60 feet from the first touchdown and then settling 35 feet farther on. In spite of this, it performed perfectly, taking some 6,000 pictures of the crater in which it landed, about 600 feet in diameter. Surveyor 3 had a small mechanized shovel attached, and on command from the earth it scooped up some grainy lunar soil and spread it out on one of the spacecraft's footpads for us to look at.

Surveyor 4 crash-landed by accident, but Surveyors 5 to 8 were complete successes. Surveyor 5 was the first of the series to carry two devices that could analyze the lunar soil. One device was a simple magnet that could be lowered into the soil and then raised and examined by televised pictures. These pictures showed the presence of magnetic material in the soil and comparisons with various earth materials showed that the moon dust acted most like powdered volcanic rock —in particular, like basalt, a volcanic material very common on the earth.

The more exact chemical analyses were made with a more complicated device that shot helium nuclei at the lunar rocks and then detected what kinds of radiation came back. These devices showed that the moon's rocks are very similar to basalt in composition, almost identical, in fact, in the case of the Surveyors that landed in lunar maria, the dark and smooth lowlands. But Surveyor 7, which landed on higher and more mountainous country near the giant crater Tycho, found a somewhat different composition, less rich in iron and other metals.

"I think it wants to shake hands."

Le Pelley *in* The Christian Science Monitor. © *TCSPS*.

Cartoonists have had lots of fun with lunar research. This drawing shows Surveyor 3 with its mechanical shovel.

The Orbiters

The first satellite to be put into orbit around the moon was the Russian Luna 10 spacecraft, which was launched at the end of March 1966. The second was the American Orbiter 1, launched five months later. Two more Russian and four more American orbiters were launched during the following twelve months, all successfully.

The main purpose of the orbiters was to map in detail the areas where manned lunar landings might take place. The American Orbiters 1 through 3 accomplished this task in short order, and presumably the Russian satellites also completed their missions. There was nothing of this sort left for Orbiters 4 and 5 to do, so it was decided to use them to form a complete and very detailed lunar atlas. Orbiter 4 took the entire earth-facing side of the moon and Orbiter 5 photographed the entire far side, producing an atlas so huge that it takes a whole room to store a copy of it. It will be many years before lunar geologists have gone over it and extracted all the important scientific data contained in this atlas. The pictures show everything on the moon larger than about 150 feet, including about 30 million craters.

Another important task of the Orbiters was to measure accurately the shape of the moon's field of gravity. For instance, Orbiter 1 first was put into a special "parking" orbit about 500 miles above the moon's surface, where it measured all the different variations in the gravity it could record. It then was lowered to about 25 miles above the surface, after the scientists working on it had used the facts it gave on the gravitational field to plan such a maneuver without endangering the craft. The most interesting scientific outcome of these tests was the fact that the density of the rock under the maria is different from the density under the mountains and highlands. These mass concentrations, or "mascons," indicate that there are large and important variations in the properties of lunar material, even deep down.

Manned Lunar Flights

The first manned flight to the area of the moon carried three American astronauts successfully to their destination on Christmas Eve, 1968. After nine orbits around the

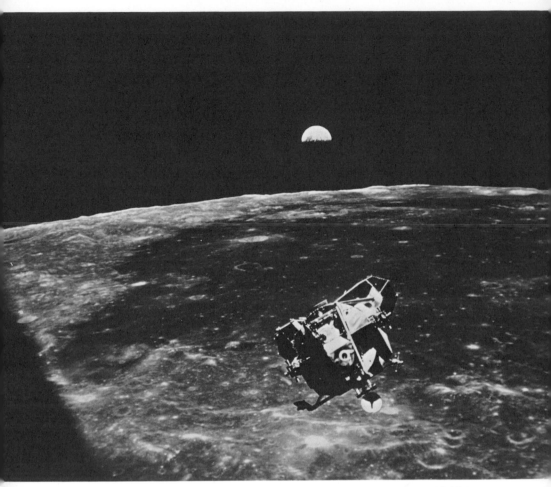

The ascent stage of the lunar module of the Apollo 11 project, after successfully reaching the moon's surface. The lower part of the module was left on the moon to serve as a launch platform. This photograph was made from the command module while the ascent stage was approaching the command module to dock to it again. The earth is seen rising above the lunar horizon.

moon, during which they photographed the satellite and the earth, and sent pictures plus verbal descriptions back to the National Aeronautics and Space Administration, they returned to a heroes' welcome. Although not as important scientifically as some of the unmanned flights, this historic trip paved the way for an outstanding scientific event, when astronauts landed on the moon and gathered samples and other data to bring back to laboratories on the earth.

This occurred on July 20, 1969, when astronauts Neil Armstrong, Edwin Aldrin, and Michael Collins steered Apollo 11 to the moon and Armstrong and Aldrin became the first men to walk on our satellite. They returned to the earth on July 24, after leaving equipment for two experiments on the Sea of Tranquility. One was a seismograph for measuring "moonquakes"; the other was a laser reflector which allows measurement of the distance to the moon to within about six inches. This uses a radar-type technique but with visual light generated by a laser attached to large optical telescopes on the earth.

The most important scientific experiments made possible by this historic trip are those performed on the many samples of lunar rock and dust that the astronauts brought back. They showed for the first time the many profound ways in which the lunar soil and rocks differ from those on the earth: their great age, their unique chemistry, the signs of their birth and deformation by meteorite impact, and the mysterious ways in which some samples are covered with a glass coating. We look to continuing Apollo missions to various other parts of the moon to bring into more and more detailed focus the long and complicated history of our satellite.

Edwin Aldrin setting up the seismic instrument on the moon's surface, to record and broadcast tremors in the body of our satellite. One array of solar cells to provide electricity has been extended at left; another was extended at the right a few moments later. The lunar module is seen in the background. Photographs made on the moon are harshly lighted and contrasty because there is no floating dust and moisture, and virtually no atmosphere, to diffuse the light as on earth.

SEVENTEEN

Exploring the Planets

"To the right of the aircraft is the summit of the highest mountain in the Pacific, Mauna Kea, 13,800 feet above sea level. As we pass its summit you will get a good view of the new observatory built there to study the planets." Thus the captain of a Hawaiian jetliner tells his passengers about one of the many new astronomical institutions built to explore the natural bodies that orbit the sun.

In order to keep a surveillance of conditions on the other planets, the National Aeronautics and Space Administration, or NASA, has financed the construction of several new large planetary telescopes. One of them, the 88-inch instrument of the University of Hawaii, was placed on the snowy top of Hawaii's highest extinct volcano, Mauna Kea, from whose cold and barren summit astronomers get a better and steadier view of the planets than from most other locations. Another NASA telescope, 107 inches in diameter and the

Saturn, visually one of the most dramatic of the bodies that revolve about the sun, is among the planets being subjected to fresh optical observation as new telescopes designed for planetary work are built to augment scans by space probes. The rings are thought to consist mainly of ammonia ice.

third largest in the world, sits on the summit of Mount Locke in western Texas, where University of Texas astronomers study planetary problems. An unusual telescope of very, very high magnifying power (to produce large planetary images) has been built in the desert mountains of central Chile, where Lowell Observatory astronomers keep track of conditions on the planets when they are in southern skies. All these new telescopes and more are needed to carry out basic observations of the planets to support and supplement the space probes that travel to them for firsthand data.

Thin Air on Mars

Mars, the most romantic of the planets because of speculation about Martian life, has been a foremost target of recent planetary scrutiny. One of the most important modern discoveries about Mars is the revelation that its atmosphere is very much thinner than previously thought.

The young California astronomer Hyron Spinrad was one of the first to discover this. It was later supported by many other revelations, including those of the first successful Mars probe. Spinrad used large earth-bound telescopes to obtain detailed spectra of the planet. He found certain dark lines on his spectra that were not from the sun (Martian light is reflected sunlight), and were therefore produced by the gas in Mars's atmosphere. These lines were mostly due to carbon dioxide, identified long before as being present. Spinrad was able, by measuring the different strengths of the lines, to deduce the total amount of pressure at the Martian surface due to its atmosphere and found it to be only about one one-hundredth the pressure at the earth's surface. Previous measures had erroneously indicated a much higher pressure. We now know, due to Spinrad's and other's earthbound measures and to the density determination carried out by Mariner 4, that Mars does have very thin air.

Craters on Mars

Perhaps the most spectacular result of the first Mars probe was the discovery of many large craters. Mariner 4, launched on November 28, 1964, reached the vicinity of

Mars seven and a half months later. It immediately took a series of 21 television pictures of part of the Martian surface and later radioed these back to the earth. It was an exciting moment when the first of these arrived. It was flashed on TV and spread out on the front pages of newspapers. But the best pictures were some of the later ones, taken with the surface under a low angle of sunlight, when the shadows made the surface relief stand out. On those pictures many craters were visible, ranging in size from two to 75 miles in diameter. As it was Martian winter at these locations, some of the raised rims of the craters were covered with frost. Shadows showed that the rims rose about 300 feet above the surrounding flat plains.

Why is Mars cratered like the moon? There are two reasons; one is that since these craters are produced by collision with meteorites, Mars gets more craters than the earth because it is closer to the asteroid belt, the source of meteorites. More important is the fact that the thin atmosphere and scarcity of water on the planet lead to a very low erosion rate for the surface. Mars's craters are several million years old, on the average, while meteorite craters on the earth cannot easily last through the weather of more than a few thousand years. On the moon, which has virtually no air at all, craters can last a billion years or more.

The Martian craters, combined with our new views of lunar craters, have caused a surge of new interest in similar impact craters on the earth. Astronomers, geologists, and physicists have rushed to make new studies of the almost 200 known terrestrial meteorite craters to find out more exactly how the explosion of impact produces what we see.

Because of the high rate of erosion in wetter places, many of the large meteorite craters on the earth are in desert

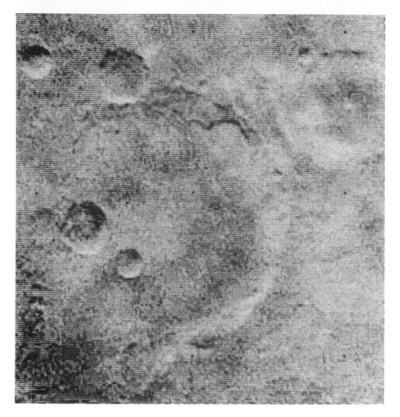

Mariner 4 made this photograph of the surface of Mars in 1965, one of many historic pictures shot by it and radioed to earth. North is at the top; the picture shows 150 miles of surface from north to south and 170 miles from east to west. The radio signals representing the image were fed into a computer after reception, and this reproduced them in picture form with the contrasts strengthened; the screen effect results from this process.

regions. There is one almost a mile across in northern Arizona, and a smaller one near Odessa, Texas. A remarkable group of 15 craters lies in the red desert of central Australia, and a chain of meteorite craters has been studied in Argentina. Some of the largest are in northern Canada, where they often turn out to be lakes, 10 miles or more across, marking the meteorites' scars in the sheet of ancient, hard rock called the Canadian shield. New studies take scientists on expeditions to these fascinating objects, and to others in such places as Arabia, South Africa, Siberia, and the Sahara.

Taking the Temperature of Venus

In 1962, when the first successful Venus probe was launched, it was already known that there was something peculiar about the temperature of Venus. Radio telescopes had shown that it had either a very high surface temperature, about 700° absolute, or else a strong ionosphere that gave spurious readings at radio wavelengths. One of the tasks of Mariner 2, launched in September 1962, was to decide which possibility was correct.

On December 14, 1962, Mariner 2 passed within 25,000 miles of Venus. It scanned the disk of the planet to measure the temperature at different locations. The results indicated that the surface is certainly very hot and that the radio telescopes' measures were correct. The probe also discovered that Venus has no detectable magnetic field, unlike the earth. It found no radiation belts like our Van Allen belts (discovered years before by the first U.S. artificial satellite). Finally, it gave us a new and better measure of the planet's mass.

It is interesting to note that one of Mariner 2's accomplishments was actually scooped by the Palomar 200-inch telescope. Before the spacecraft was able to make its scans of the surface temperature, two young astronomers used the earth's largest telescope to do the same job. The large size of this instrument gave them about the same view of the planet as that of the much nearer but much smaller telescope on the probe. This fact illustrates the importance of the ingenious use of large terrestrial telescopes for planetary exploration. But of course the space probes are very necessary too, as the other experiments carried out by Mariner 2 could not have been done by an earth telescope.

Favorable conditions for a launch to Venus occur about every $1\text{-}^6\!/_{10}$ years. The next Venus shot, therefore, had to wait until another close approach. The one of April 1964 was passed up, but the next one, in November 1965, was used by the U.S.S.R., which launched Venera 2 toward Venus then. But little new data were learned until the 1967 launch opportunity, when two spacecraft went to Venus on nearly identical paths.

The Race to Venus

In June 1967, within two days of each other, America's Mariner 5 and Russia's Venera 4 were launched on a 200-million-mile race to Venus. Many of the experiments carried on board were identical, but the much larger Soviet vehicle carried as well a capsule that eventually parachuted down through the Venusian atmosphere as the first man-made object to send back data from the surface of another planet with an atmosphere.

Venera 4 and Mariner 5 made hundreds of important new measurements of conditions on Venus and in its neighborhood. They tested for a magnetic field, with a negative answer. They determined just how Venus protects itself from the solar wind, the stream of particles that are con-

tinually ejected from the sun toward the planets. Both spacecraft agreed that the solar-wind particles are stopped from
bombarding the Venus surface by the planet's ionosphere.
(In the case of the earth the magnetic field does this).

When they had nearly reached the planet, the two spacecraft took different paths. Mariner 5 swung around Venus,
passing within 2,600 miles of its surface before proceeding
into interplanetary space. All of its probing of the Venusian
atmosphere was done by passing various radio waves
through it to the earth as the craft was eclipsed by Venus.
The Venera 4 vehicle instead penetrated right into the
planet's atmosphere, automatically releasing a parachute-
equipped capsule that floated slowly down toward the surface. Both craft obtained information on the upper atmosphere of Venus, but only Venera 4 sent back direct data on
the lower atmosphere, near the surface.

Air Everywhere, but None to Breathe

The atmosphere of Venus is very different from our
own. It has a thin outer layer of hydrogen (captured from
the solar wind), much thinner than the earth's and about
600 miles above the surface. Below that is an ionosphere,
with two peaks in density, one 60 and the other 50 miles
above the surface.

The bulk of the atmosphere lies lower. According to the
Mariner 5 data, the atmosphere is so thick that at the surface
there is 65 times as much air pressure as at sea level on the
earth. Such a dense atmosphere would be suffocating even
if it contained oxygen. The Venera 4 data indicated a smaller
pressure, some 20 times the earth's, but it is now believed
that what was originally thought to be a surface measure-

ment by Venera 4 was actually made at a considerable altitude, and that the capsule for some unknown reason mismeasured its height and stopped working long before it hit the ground.

The surface temperature estimated from Mariner 5 measures is 700° absolute (about 800° F.), in agreement with earlier measurements. Venera 4 detected a 100° cooler temperature at the time it stopped.

Before these space flights, it was known from ground-based observatories that Venus had a good deal of carbon dioxide in its atmosphere. But Venera 4 and Mariner 5 gave more exact values of the amounts of this and other gases present. Venera 4 reported from its automatic chemical measurements that carbon dioxide makes up between 90 and 95 per cent of the atmosphere. The rest is mostly nitrogen and/or neon. The Russian results also indicated about 1 per cent oxygen, but this is not supported by ground-based measures that rule out more than one-thousandth of 1 per cent of oxygen. This disagreement has not been resolved.

The amount of water in Venus' atmosphere is very small. According to Venera 4, there is only a few tenths of 1 per cent present. Because the temperature is so high that no oceans could exist, this atmospheric water must be all that the planet has. Totaled up, Venus has only about one ten-thousandth as much water as the earth has, in spite of the almost exactly equal size of the two planets.

Mariners 6 and 7

The 1969 flybys of Mariners 6 and 7 past Mars produced a

number of exciting new discoveries about the red planet. It
detected thin haze in patches, 10 to 25 miles up. A mysterious
brightening, so far unexplained, occurs in the "W-cloud"
area, a large part of the Martian surface where ground-

The south polar cap of Mars, taken by a television camera on
Mariner 7 in August 1969, as the spacecraft neared its closest
approach to the planet. The picture was taken at an altitude of
about 3,300 miles and covers an area of approximately 740 by
930 miles. Three large craters and a number of smaller ones
can be seen. There is a cloudlike formation at the upper left
and near it ridges suggesting the snowdrifts we see on earth,
though it is uncertain that these are true snow.

NASA

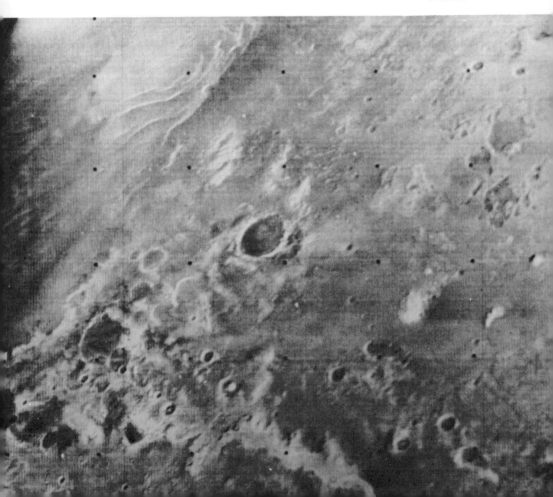

based telescopes have reported an apparent cloudlike feature shaped like a W. What may be low, hazy clouds were seen over the polar ice cap. The "snow" of the cap is variable in thickness, probably because of wind drifting. The ice is most probably "dry ice" (CO_2), not water ice, and is several inches thick. Craters abound, though not as thickly as on the moon. Two other types of terrain were also discovered, one of which is jumbled, torn up, and chaotic, the other smooth and featureless. Because there are few or no craters in these areas, it is supposed that some more recent event or events must have produced them. Some kind of geologic process apparently is at work, though it is different from the common ones that have produced our earthly terrain.

Why are there so many differences between Venus, Mars, and the earth? They are mysteries that still puzzle us in spite of our new knowledge from experimentation by spacecraft. We hope to find the answers to these and other questions as man's greatest adventure, the exploration of the planets, continues.

Suggested Reading

Chapter 2

J. L. Steinberg and J. Lequeux, *Radio Astronomy* (McGraw-Hill, New York, 1962)

Grote Reber, "Radio Astronomy" (*Scientific American*, Sept. 1949)

R. W. Clarke, "Locating Radio Sources with the Moon" (*Scientific American*, June 1966)

B. J. Bok, "Radio Astronomy and the Galactic System" (*Sky and Telescope*, Dec. 1966)

A. H. Barrett, "Radio Signals from Hydroxyl Radicals" (*Scientific American*, Dec. 1968)

Chapter 3

G. R. Burbidge and F. Hoyle, "The Problem of the Quasi-Stellar Objects" (*Scientific American*, Dec. 1966)

Chapter 4

P. W. Hodge, *Concepts of the Universe* (McGraw-Hill, New York, 1969)

A. R. Sandage, "Exploding Galaxies" (*Scientific American*, Nov. 1964)

Chapter 5

P. J. E. Peebles and D. T. Wilkenson, "The Primeval Fireball" (*Scientific American*, June 1967)

Chapter 6

A. G. W. Cameron and S. P. Maran, "The Enigmatic Pulsars" (*Sky and Telescope*, July 1968)

A. Hewish, "Pulsars" (*Scientific American*, Oct. 1968)

Chapter 7

K. L. Franklin, "Radio Waves from Jupiter" (*Scientific American*, July 1964)

Chapter 8

I. I. Shapiro, "Radar Observations of the Planets" (*Scientific American*, July 1968)

Chapter 9

B. C. Murray and J. A. Westphal, "Infrared Astronomy" (*Scientific American*, Aug. 1965)

J. Strong, "Infrared Astronomy by Balloon" (*Scientific American*, Jan. 1965)

H. L. Johnson, "Infrared Stars" (*Sky and Telescope*, Aug. 1966)

G. Neugebauer and R. B. Leighton, "The Infrared Sky" (*Scientific American*, Aug. 1968)

Chapter 10

K. G. Henije and L. R. Wackerling, "Stellar Ultraviolet Spectra from Gemini 10" (*Sky and Telescope*, Oct. 1966)

R. N. Watts, Jr., "OSO 4 Ultraviolet Solar Observations" (*Sky and Telescope*, Dec. 1967)

Chapter 11

H. Friedman, "X-Ray Astronomy" (*Scientific American*, June 1964)

H. Gursky, "Identification of the X-ray Source in Scorpius" (*Sky and Telescope,* Nov. 1966)

Chapter 12

C. F. Fichtel, "Gamma-Ray Astronomy" (*Sky and Telescope,* Feb. 1968)

Chapter 13

F. Reines and J. P. F. Sellschop, "Neutrinos from the Atmosphere and Beyond" (*Scientific American,* Feb. 1966)

Chapter 14

G. R. Burbidge, "The Origins of Cosmic Rays" (*Scientific American,* Aug. 1966)

A. N. Bunner, "High-Energy Cosmic Rays" (*Sky and Telescope,* Oct. 1967)

Chapter 15

C. A. Lundquist, *Space Science* (McGraw-Hill, New York, 1966)

H. E. Newell, H. J. Smith, N. G. Roman, and G. E. Mueller (National Aeronautics and Space Administration, Washington, D.C., 1967; publication no. NASA SP-127)

Chapter 16

Z. Kopal, *Exploration of the Moon by Spacecraft* (Oliver and Boyd, London, 1968)

H. M. Schurmeier, R. L. Heacock, and A. E. Wolfe, "The Ranger Missions to the Moon" (*Scientific American,* Jan. 1966)

"Some Surveyor Findings" (*Sky and Telescope,* Aug. 1966)

R. N. Watts, Jr., "Surveyor 3 on the Moon" (*Sky and Telescope,* June 1967)

Y. N. Lipski, "What Luna 9 Told Us About the Moon" (*Sky and Telescope,* Nov. 1966)

A. R. Hibbs, "The Surface of the Moon" (*Scientific American,* March 1967)

R. N. Watts, Jr., "Lunar Orbiter Surveys the Moon" (*Sky and Telescope,* Oct. 1966)

———, "Results From Lunar Orbiter 2" (*Sky and Telescope,* Jan. 1967)

———, "Lunar Orbiter 4" (*Sky and Telescope,* July 1967)

———, "Orbiter 5" (*Sky and Telescope,* Oct. 1967)

E. Levin, D. D. Viele, and L. B. Eldrenkamp, "The Lunar Orbiter Missions to the Moon" (*Scientific American,* May 1968)

Chapter 17

J. N. James, "The Voyage of Mariner IV" (*Scientific American,* March 1966)

R. B. Leighton, "The Photographs From Mariner IV" (*Scientific American,* April 1966)

Richard K. Sloan, "The Scientific Experiments of Mariner IV" (*Scientific American,* May 1966)

Books and Booklets

Isaac Asimov, *The Double Planet* (Abelard-Schuman, New York, 1966)

Alfred Bester, *The Life and Death of a Satellite* (Little, Brown, Boston, 1966)

Franklyn M. Branley, *Experiments in Sky Watching* (T. Y. Crowell, New York, 1967)

———, *Mars: Planet Number Four* (T. Y. Crowell, New York, 1966)

Richard M. Harbeck and Lloyd K. Johnson, *Earth and Space Science* (Holt, New York, 1965)

Fred Hoyle, *Man in the Universe* (Columbia Univ. Press, New York, 1966)

J. Allen Hynek and Norman D. Anderson, *Challenge of the Universe* (Scholastic, New York, 1965; paperback)

Willy Ley, *Ranger to the Moon* (Signet, New York, 1965; paperback)

Patrick Moore, *The New Look of the Universe* (Norton, New York, 1966)

———, *The Sky at Night* (Norton, New York, 1965)

National Aerospace Education Council, *Aerospace Bibliography* (4th ed.; available from Supt. of Documents, U. S. Govt. Printing Office, Washington, D.C. 20402)

Magazines

Review of Popular Astronomy (Sky Map Publications, 111 So. Meramec, St. Louis, Mo. 63105)

Science News (1719 N St., NW, Washington, D.C. 20036)

Scientific American (415 Madison Ave., New York, N.Y. 10017)

Sky and Telescope (Sky Publishing Corp., 49 Bay State Road, Cambridge, Mass. 02138)

Space World (Palmer Publications, Rt. 2, Box 36, Amherst, Wis. 54406)

Glossary

angstrom: A unit of length equal to 10^{-8} centimeter.

antimatter: Material made up of elementary particles with properties that are opposite (for example, opposite in charge) to those that make up the matter in our familiar universe. Antimatter, when brought into contact with matter, leads to complete annihilation.

asteroid: Small planet-like object with its orbit primarily concentrated between the orbits of Mars and Jupiter. The largest asteroids are several hundred miles in diameter and the smallest detectable ones are approximately a mile in diameter. There are many thousands of known asteroids.

astronomical unit: The average distance between the earth and the sun, a fundamental unit in many applications of astronomical distance measurement.

the big bang: A popular name for a plausible theory of the origin of the universe which explains the present expansion of the universe in terms of an explosive beginning about 10 billion years ago.

corona: The outer extremely hot and very sparse atmosphere of the sun.

cosmic rays: Tiny, extremely high-energy particles produced by the sun and by much more distant sources in the galaxy. Cosmic rays are primarily protons, but include also much heavier particles that are the nuclei of heavy atoms, and some gamma rays.

Crab nebula: The gas cloud that remains from the explosion of a supernova observed by Chinese astronomers in the year 1054 A.D.

electromagnetic radiation: This term includes light and all similar types of wavelike radiation: radio waves, gamma waves, X rays, and ultraviolet and infrared waves. The entire group is called the electromagnetic spectrum.

electron: A small negatively charged elementary particle that exists in the outer parts of atoms.

electron volt: A small unit of energy that is equivalent to the energy acquired by an electron which passes through a one-volt difference in potential.

galaxy: A huge organization of stars that is held together by its own gravity. Galaxies contain between a million and a million million stars.

gamma rays: Electromagnetic radiation with wavelengths shorter than the X rays (less than a few tenths of an angstrom).

hadrons: Elementary particles that interact strongly. Hadrons include protons, neutrons, and various other high-mass elementary particles plus mesons.

ionosphere: That portion of the upper atmosphere of the earth or other planet that is ionized, meaning that solar radiation or particles have removed electrons from the atoms of the upper atmosphere at this position.

leptons: The small elementary particles, including electrons, neutrinos, and muons.

long-period variable: Cool, highly evolved stars that pulsate slowly with periods thaat can be anywhere between approximately 100 and 1,000 days.

maria: The Latin term for "seas," used for the moon and Mars, to designate areas that appear darker and smoother than their surroundings. In neither case do the maria contain water.

maser: A device (either artificially constructed or found naturally in interstellar space) that is able to concentrate all energy or light into a given narrow wavelength band. The word is coined from the initials of Microwave Amplification by Stimulated Emission of Radiation.

mesons: Those elementary particles that have mass intermediate between the largest (protons and neutrons) and the smallest (e.g., electrons). Mesons are unstable.

meteorite: A meteor which is large enough to reach all the way to the ground without being completely melted or fragmented as it passes through the earth's atmosphere. Meteorites are primarily of two types, either metallic, made up mostly of iron and nickel, or stony, with a composition somewhat like terrestrial stones. They apparently originate as a result of collisions of asteroids in the asteroid belt between Mars and Jupiter.

meteors: Small objects, ranging in size from a fraction of an inch up to several feet, which produce a bright flash of light as they collide with the earth's atmosphere. Most meteors are debris from the break-up of comets. A few apparently have originated in the asteroid belt, between the orbits of Mars and Jupiter.

muons: Tiny unstable particles first thought to be related to the mesons but less massive than the objects now considered true mesons.

neutrino: A tiny elementary particle without charge and without any mass except that due to relativity.

neutron: An elementary particle without charge, of approximately the same mass as a proton, and similarly found in the nuclei of atoms.

neutron stars: Stars that have collapsed to such small size and high density that all atoms have lost their identity and the material is primarily in the form of neutrons.

nonthermal sources: Observed sources of radio and other radiation that emit waves for reasons other than the temperature of the object.

nova: An explosive star which in ejecting a portion of its outer layers becomes unusually bright for a short period of time.

OAO: Abbreviation for the series of astronomical observatories launched on satellites, called Orbiting Astronomical Observatories.

OSO: Abbreviation for the Orbiting Solar Observatories.

photons: Tiny quantum collections of light energy or that of other electromagnetic radiation. Light behaves sometimes like waves and sometimes like particles, and in the latter case these particles are called photons.

plasma: A cloud of charged particles.

proton: An elementary particle with a positive charge, more massive than the electron, and existing in the nuclei of atoms.

pulsars: Radio sources that exhibit extremely short pulses of radiation. A few also are observable at other wavelengths, including optical and X-ray wavelengths. They are believed to be neutron stars, stars with extremely high density and small size, that are rotating.

quantum mechanics: The mathematical equations by which physicists are able to describe and understand the behavior of small-scale events, involving elementary particles.

quasar: Also known as "quasi-stellar objects," these are small, intensely bright and apparently distant gas clouds that emit strong optical and (usually) radio radiation. Many have very large shifts to the red in their spectra, probably indicating very large distances.

radiation belts: Areas surrounding the earth (or other planet) that contain captured charged particles that oscillate back and forth in the magnetic field of the planet. The earth's radiation belts were first discovered by Van Allen, using the first U.S. satellite.

red shift: The displacement of spectral lines in the spectrum of an object, caused by that object's apparent recession from us in space.

Seyfert galaxies: Galaxies with extremely bright nuclei containing gas clouds with high temperatures and showing high velocities.

spectral lines: Dark or bright lines in the spectrum of an object that indicate either absorption or emission of radiation at a specific wavelength by a specific chemical element.

spectrum: The light of an object which has been separated into its different wavelength components. Red light is at one end of the optical spectrum and violet at the other. The word can also refer to the total electromagnetic spectrum.

supernova: An explosive star which becomes much brighter than a nova because of the fact that the entire star has exploded away into space.

synchrotron radiation: A type of nonthermal radiation that is emitted when charged particles are moving at extremely rapid speeds in a magnetic field.

wavelength: The characteristic length of the waves that make up light or other kinds of wavelike radiation. Ordinary light has very small wavelengths whereas radio waves have comparatively long wavelengths.

white dwarf stars: Small faint stars that have reached the final stages in their evolution and radiate only by virtue of their remaining thermal energy.

X rays: Electromagnetic radiation of very short wavelengths, between approximately 400 angstroms and a fraction of an angstrom.

Index

absolute temperature, 23
Aldrin, Edwin, 163, 164
Andromeda galaxy, 10
antimatter, 39, 40, 62
Apollo spacecraft, 147, 162, 163
Arecibo radio telescope, 19, 21
Armstrong, Neil, 163
asteroids, 93, 148
astronomical unit, 93
atmospheric turbulence, 148

balloons, 128-133
baryons, 59, 61, 65
"big bang," 54-67
Burke, Bernard, 82, 83

carbon stars, 104
Collins, Michael, 163
cool stars, 104
cosmic background radiation, 67
cosmic rays, 108, 139-145
CP 1919, 70, 72-73
Crab Nebula, 73, 75, 77, 121, 122, 133, 145

diffraction grating, 110

Einstein, Albert, 144
Einstein's relativity formula, 135, 143-144
electromagnetic radiation, 19
electron volt, 141